PRECIOUS MEMORIES

Lovingly and affectionately dedicated
to the memory of my husband,
Virgil O. Stamps

Mrs. V. O. Stamps

Virgil O. Stamps

Precious Memories

of

VIRGIL O. STAMPS

●

Leatherette Cloth Cover

$1.00 per copy, prepaid

●

Stamps-Baxter Music and Printing Company

DALLAS, TEXAS — CHATTANOOGA, TENN. — PANGBURN, ARK.

Biographical Sketch

"Let the word of Christ dwell in you richly in all wisdom; teaching and admonishing one another in psalms and hymns and spiritual songs, singing with grace in your hearts to the Lord."

—*Colossians III, 16.*

Many Texans, whose memories will live long in the annals of the State, first saw the light of day in the piney woods of East Texas which, through the years, have become synonymous with honesty and integrity—to be associated with steadfast, reliable men, whose achievements constitute not alone a noble example, but also a heritage. Amid such inspirational surroundings, there came into the world, in Upshur County, on September 18, 1892, a boy, the fourth of six sons born to Mr. and Mrs. W. O. Stamps. By his mother, the lusty youngster was christened "Virgil Oliver."

Life in East Texas at that time was not one of ease and luxury; hard work was regarded as a virtue and men labored for the benefits that they received. For several years, Virgil Oliver Stamps' father represented his district in the State's Legislature, but it was as a "sawmiller" that, by dint of hard toil, he for many years made a "good living" for himself and his growing family from the virgin forests of that region. Thus, young Virgil's early surroundings were relatively humble, but both W. O. Stamps and his wife were devout Christians and it was in a God-fearing home that the boy matured.

The voice, ability, friendliness and, above all, the sincerity of this youngster were to carry him far along his chosen path. In East Texas, the "singing convention" is a time-honored institution; in his childhood, there developed in this "sawmill youngster" an unquenchable love of music—an especial fondness for the old-fashioned gospel hymns—that was to endure.

In his early 'teens, the boy attended a session of the Upshur County Singing Convention and it was there that, for the first time, he heard a quartet sing. Thrilled to his very core by their harmony, it was then that the young Stamps resolved that he himself would learn to sing. And that resolution, later, made his name one of the most widely-known among lovers of quartet singing anywhere.

There were few "singing teachers" in that "woods country" in those days, but from such instructors as the county afforded, the boy learned what he could. He bought every book upon musical subjects that he could find and spent hours, days and weeks assiduously mastering their contents, hungry for the knowledge that they could impart. Later, grown older, he decided to go away to school, but by that time financial reverses had overtaken the family. Undismayed, the youth adhered to his ambition, but was obliged to borrow heavily. As a result, he succeeded in getting a musical education, but at the same time he acquired debts that it took him years and years to pay.

BIOGRAPHICAL SKETCH

In 1907 young Virgil attended his first singing school, taught by R. M. Morgan. Specializing in music and voice culture, he continued his studies, and from 1911 to 1914, while working in a store which his father had acquired at Ore City, in Upshur County, he taught singing schools in his spare time. It was in the latter year that he became a composer—at the age of 22, he wrote his first song "Man Behind the Plow", which he had printed on sheets and sold for 10c a copy.

Encouraged by these ventures, it was in 1914 that he resolved to devote his entire time to music. He obtained employment with a music concern, but always a student, he took every opportunity to learn more of music and singing, while continuing active in the teaching of others to sing. Thus, he entered upon his life's work which, henceforward, was to have to do wholly with music, in one form or another.

He broadened not only his acquaintance but also his experience, through the years and coincidentally, he enhanced a growing reputation both as a singer and a teacher of singing. He worked in Texas for a Tennessee Music Co. until 1917, when he went to Atlanta, Georgia, for another company; in 1918 he moved to Lawrenceburg to work again for the Tennessee concern. In 1919, he came back to Texas, locating first at Timpson but moving a year later to Jacksonville, there to open a branch office of a music publishing company. In all of these places, he continued to sing and to teach singing, convinced that most persons, afforded the opportunity, not only enjoy good singing but wish to sing themselves.

By the help of his friends he first went into business for himself in Jacksonville, Texas, in 1924, establishing there the V. O. Stamps Music Company. In that year, he published his first book of songs "Harbor Bells," which is still in print today. This publication was an instant success, the sales not only far exceeding those of any similar book issued by a new concern, but also surpassing sales records made by many old-established publishing companies.

In March, 1926, J. R. Baxter, Jr., one of the outstanding musicians of the country, became associated with the Stamps concern, and in 1927, the name of the company was changed to The Stamps-Baxter Music Company. Baxter and "V. O." had become great friends over a period of years, during which time, they represented competitive music publishing companies. They became partners and sole owners of the business with Mr. Stamps, serving as president, and continuing to maintain an office in Jacksonville; Mr. Baxter, vice president, opened an office in Chattanooga, Tennessee. In 1929 the Texas office was moved to Dallas.

In Jacksonville and later in Dallas, for a time, the company's song books were printed in Dalton, Georgia, but ultimately it was decided that the concern should print its own books. So, printing machinery was bought and a small printing and publishing business started on Beckley Avenue, in 1934.

This venture, thriving from the start, necessitated moving the business, now known as the Stamps-Baxter Music and Printing Company, to more commodious quarters at its present location, 209-11 South Tyler Street, in 1936. There its facilities were further enlarged from time to time as the business continued to grow, until today the Stamps-Baxter Company is reputed to be the largest printing business on earth devoted exclusively to the publishing of gospel music and songs. In its present quarters, the concern sets its own type, owning the largest and most complete music type-setting plant in the United States; they print song books by the millions on the most modern automatic presses and the number of their employees has been increased from time to time as the growth of the business required. Today, aside from the offices in Dallas and Chattanooga, an office is also maintained in Pangburn, Arkansas.

From the up-to-date plant in Dallas, books go forth to every State in the American Union, and into every English-speaking foreign nation; literally they have been printed by the millions. While most publishers were satisfied with producing one new song book annually, this concern led the field in first putting out a successful "mid-season" book; and only a few weeks before Mr. Stamps' death he announced a new schedule, calling for four books each year on a subscription plan such as is used by magazines.

The books are interdenominational; Virgil Stamps, a member of the Methdist Church, worked with people of all faiths, believing that there were many consecrated Christians in every church under the sun. On the firm's staff of writers are many famous gospel-song composers of various denominations, whose songs appear only in Stamps-Baxter books.

The Stamps-Baxter concern constantly has expanded its activities, including the founding of the Stamps-Baxter School of Music, in which thousands of music lovers have learned to sing. At a recent session of the school over 500 pupils enrolled from some twenty-two States. At the time of his death, Mr. Stamps was editor of the "Gospel Music News", a monthly publication with a distribution of 50,000 scattered throughout every State in the United States. He was President of the Texas State Singers Association and served in that capacity from the time he organized it until his death; he was founder and an active member of the famous Stamps Quartet which is known everywhere that gospel music is sung.

To hundreds of thousands of gospel-music lovers over the entire nation during the past few years, an inspiration has been the deep-timbered melodious voice of V. O. Stamps that came to them daily over Station KRLD, Dallas. The enunciation of brief gospel messages were interpersed by religious melodies through the magnificent powerful basso of Virgil Stamps, that welled forth in its full strength and beauty as the Stamps Quartet broadcast the "oldtime" religion in song.

The remarkable success which crowned the efforts of Mr. Stamps and his singing associates was not measured by him in terms of mere pecuniary reward. To him, it represented, more definitely, the culmination and achievement of his life-long mission to carry gospel music to the masses, and with it the word of God. It pleased him most that the results of his quartet's renditions, as indicated by ever-increasing letters, evidenced existence of a new field of religious work, of a scope that could not be reached by any other known means. In his heart was the great desire to make the world happier and better through gospel songs.

V. O. Stamps believed firmly that those whose religion had been for a long time merely conventional, or dormant, or even something flatly rejected, might be turned to the God of their fathers by a kindly, helpful word. His soothing voice served to lighten the burdens of many who were oppressed.

Thus, one man wrote to him: "The singing and brief messages throughout the program made me begin to think about Christianity. After a few weeks I was converted and joined the church." Another related how his "sleeping conscience" was aroused when "in a beer-joint, partially intoxicated", he heard one of the gospel songs over the radio. He wrote: "Your gospel singing has helped to change my life, and caused me to become a Christian and an active member of the church."

Such letters have been numerous, as have commendatory words from members of churches and ministers of the gospel; all are but added pearls in the crown of V. O. Stamps' achievements. Before his death he had succeeded in his self-imposed task of carrying gospel music to those in every nook and corner of the land. But the road to this end had been long and hard to travel; often penniless in his earlier days, he persisted despite difficulties that were discouraging indeed. Nevertheless, he was tenatious, and little by little, his work became recognized.

V. O. Stamps was the type of man who was bound to make friends. There was no hypocrisy about him; he was always sincere yet he possessed an unusual sense of humor. His was a wholesome personality. His voice not alone was big and strong, for physically he was a big man and his heart was big. He really loved to sing and to teach others to sing; he loved the beauty and harmony of music. Not only did he pioneer the singing of religious songs over radio, but many of those thus carried into the homes, were written lovingly with the rich gift of his own talent. Almost from childhood, he had realized the import of the words of the Scriptures: "Sing unto the Lord a new song, and His praise from the end of the earth . . . Let the wilderness and cities thereof lift up their voice; let the inhabitants sing." To that end, he shaped his aims.

Virgil Stamps' greatest success possibly dates from the day when the Stamps Quartet first "went on the air". In itself, this great singing group constitutes striking evidence of the manner in which the radio reaches into the hearts and homes of the people. When first the Quartet proposed to broadcast gospel songs, there were skeptics who could foresee only failure.

BIOGRAPHICAL SKETCH

But the success of the venture has been surprising indeed. Subsequent to Mr. Stamps' death, in dedicating a program in appreciative remembrance, Jesse Milburn of Station KRLD expressed the opinion:

> "It is doubtful if the passing of a radio personality, since the death of Will Rogers, has so profoundly affected such a vast number of people."

The Quartet made its radio debut in Dallas early in 1936 and in the summer of that year was "on the air" at the Texas Centennial Exposition, also in Dallas. The warmth of the reception accorded these initial efforts was such that, due to contacts made at the Exposition, a regular program was instituted from Station KRLD, Dallas, in the fall of the same year. Subsequently, these popular singers have been broadcasting from one to four programs daily over KRLD for over four years without a break.

The Stamps Quartet has sung to the largest radio audiences that ever attended broadcasts in the Southwest. Of outstanding success has been the all-night singing conventions, now held annually at the close of the yearly sessions of the Stamps-Baxter School of Music. Two have been staged in the Cotton Bowl of the State Fair Park and another in the Sportatorium in Dallas.

The first, in 1938, drew a tremendous throng. The second, in 1939, also was a huge success despite adverse circumstances, a heavy downpour of rain becoming a severe test of the intense interest manifest by those attending. In 1940, over 10,000 persons were in attendance for the continuous program which began at 8 p. m. and lasted until the next morning at 7 a. m., being broadcast for eight straight hours.

Such results clearly justified Mr. Stamps' own interest in singing conventions; possibly he himself traveled more miles than any other person in the country to attend such gatherings. Years ago he rode on horseback to get to them; later he acquired a buggy, still later he travelled by automobile, and during the latter years of his life, made long trips by airplane.

The Stamps Quartet's singing has been an attraction at most of the big singing conventions for the past few years. Via the radio, their songs have become familiar to millions of listeners. So great has been the public demand for their gospel-singing that Mr. Stamps equipped his business with one of the best recording machines available, so that their voices in song could be transcribed for other radio stations. Transcriptions of their programs have been broadcast over several border stations and other stations in many parts of the United States.

Due to his intitial radio success, Mr. Stamps at the time of his death, had under his direct supervision about a dozen other quartets, singing over various broadcasting stations. His confidence in the efficacy of this mode of reaching the public was so great that he was seeking to secure a license for a broadcasting station of his own in Dallas, which doubtless he would have accomplished had he lived.

Virgil Stamps' greatest pleasure perhaps came through his teaching—the lending of a helping hand to others who desired to sing. Each year he conducted without profit and oft-times at a financial loss, singing schools for hundreds of boys and girls, men and women. Recalling his own trying struggles to attain the goal he sought, he rejoiced in making the pathway easier for other young people with music in their souls.

His success as a teacher was outstanding and almost phenomenal. Not only, under his instruction, have there been some notable composers and singers developed, but also many of his pupils have become teachers of music and singing in their turn, or choir and singing class directors. Several have become heads of music departments of colleges; others are at the head of music instruction in first-class high schools of the State. In all of their achievements, Virgil Stamps took great pride.

As regards his primal interest in life, Virgil Stamps perhaps best epitomized an oft-repeated assertion of his own. On numerous occasions, he declared that he "would rather write one good song, a song that would reach the hearts of men, women, boys and girls, than to be President of the United States."

The honesty of his aspirations undeniably were evidenced—for many people asked him to run for Governor, offered to finance his campaign and elect him should he consent to make the race. His ambitions, however, were not political, but, though he never sought or held a public office, he found time despite his manifold activities, to concern himself with the public weal.

Greatly interested in crime prevention, primarily among the young, he firmly believed that it could be accomplished best through educational means—just as he believed "stray sheep" could be brought into the fold through hearing of God. Although calls upon his time were indeed numerous, for two years previous to his passing he had labored actively for the establishment of a division of the State Department of Education to that especial end. The bill that he originated and brought to the attention of the Texas Legislature is also to be urged upon the law-making bodies of every State in the Union; when enacted into laws it is expected to make possible the saving of thousands of boys and girls from becoming launched upon careers of crime.

For the advancement of such a cause—the welfare of the youth of the nation, undeniably he was well-qualified both by temperament and by inclination. No cause could find an abler advocate than in this man of indefatigable energies, able to approach on even terms those of any social strata or class.

X

BIOGRAPHICAL SKETCH

Virgil Stamps was one who truly appreciated friendships, and friendships he acquired galore. Significant of the high esteem and respect that his life and deeds entailed were his funeral rites, when thousands assembled in sorrowing tribute for a man they really loved. Amid those thousands who passed his bier, there walked many who evidenced their wealth and affluence, but with others fortune, seemingly, had been less kind.

Negroes were permitted to pay their respects; "V. O." had many colored friends and had sung for the negroes many times.

Messages of condolence, in great numbers, came from persons in every walk of life. To the Dallas Times-Herald came 3,156 requests in one day for copies of its page on which was reproduced his likeness in connection with the notice of his death and the funeral arrangements, after radio announcement that they could be obtained. Friendly and genial by nature, and intensely human, aptly Virgil Stamps was termed "the man with a million friends."

This was but natural, for to literally hundreds of worthy causes he had given unselfish aid. Giving concerts of gospel music each year for the raising of funds for organized charities were part of this busy man's life. Children found an especial place in his heart; through his agency and cooperation hundreds of unfortunate "shut-ins," the sick and aged were made recipients of radio receiving sets. His broad understanding and womanlike tenderness were as a bulwark to the distress and suffering; often he, with his quartet, went to the bedsides of the crippled and ailing to sing the songs that brought cheer to weary hearts.

Kindly and generous, ever ready to aid any one in need, he was truly a Christian and was ready, August 19, 1940, to answer God's call to him. Conscious to the end, several hours before his passing he said to his friends, "My house is in order and I am ready to go."

Virgil Stamps will be missed by many—especially he will be missed by the song and music lovers of the nation. His splendid voice is silenced now, or less is beyond human ken, but the great work to which he devoted his life and labors goes on; the organizations he fostered still live and will continue to live. His co-workers will strive earnestly to adhere to the precepts he observed so faithfully and to emulate the example in living that he gave. For the greater good of posterity is the noble disinterestedness of one who, forgetful of self, could and did evidence tried and proved merit and fruitful virtues. And the songs that Virgil O. Stamps loved so well—the songs that he published, wrote and sang—will never die.

THOUSANDS will remember the song, "Precious Memories", as sung by the original Stamps Quartet with the rich basso of our beloved Virgil O. Stamps—this song was one of his favorite hymns and since "Precious Memories" was suggested by thousands, and decided upon for the name of this memorial book, we are making it the preface song of this publication.

Precious Memories

J. B. F. W.   Stamps-Baxter Music & Ptg. Co., owners   J. B. F. Wright

1. Precious mem'ries, un-seen an-gels, Sent from somewhere to my soul;
2. Precious fa-ther, lov-ing moth-er, Fly a-cross the lone-ly years;
3. In the still-ness of the midnight, Echoes from the past I hear;
4. As I trav-el on life's pathway, Know not what the years may hold,

How they lin-ger, ev-er near me, And the sa-cred past un-fold.
And old home scenes of my childhood, In fond mem-o-ry ap-pears.
Old-time sing-ing, glad-ness bringing, From that lovely land somewhere.
As I pon-der, hope grows fonder, Precious mem'ries flood my soul.

Chorus

Precious mem'ries, how they lin-ger, How they ev-er flood my soul,

In the still-ness of the midnight, Precious, sacred scenes unfold.

No. 1   Love is the Key

Copyright, 1940, by Stamps-Baxter Music and Ptg. Co.
in "Golden Key"

V. O. S.   Virgil O. Stamps

1. For God so loved this sin - ful world,   He gave His on - ly Son to
2. His bless - ed who - so - ev - er will   Is heard thru-out the world to -
3. Go tell the bless - ed news a - broad, That all who will may en - ter

die;   To o - pen wide the way of life,   Love is the
day,   The door of life He o - pened wide,   Love is the
in;   The Sav - ior stands with out-stretched hands, Love is the

Chorus

key, the gold - en key.   Love is the key, the gold - en key,
key,   yes,   the gold-en key,

The key that o - pened heaven's door;   And all who will may en - ter

in,   Love is the key, the gold - en key.
love is the key.

No. 2
When I Found Him

in "Golden Key"

Herbert Buffum

Virgil O. Stamps

Chorus

1. I found more than I ev-er ex-pect-ed
2. I found peace I had sought un-a-vail-ing When I found Him, I found
3. I found joy which my soul o-ver-flow-eth

rich-es I long had re-ject-ed
pow-er that was all pre-vail-ing When I found Him.
love which the saints a-lone know-eth

I found

When I

found Him, when I found Je-sus my King, When He found me He
my Sav-ior, me lone-ly

gave me a new song to sing; When He came in He light-ed the shad-ows so
in quick-ly

dim And now I am tell-ing the joys that are mine Since I found Him.

Does Your Life Count for God?

V. O. S.

Virgil O. Stamps, owner, 1919

Virgil O. Stamps

1. As you live your life each day, Do you while your time a-way? Does your
2. Do you speak a word of cheer To a down-cast brother here? Does your
3. As you jour-ney on the road, To the Sav-ior's blest a-bode, Does your

life count for God each day? When you see a man in need, Are you then a
life count for God each day? Do you tell Him of the love Of the Sav-ior
life count for God each day? Are you turn-ing err-ing men From the path of

Chorus

friend in deed? Does your life count for God each day?
dear a-bove; Does your life count for God each day? Does your life count for God?
vice and sin; Does your life count for God each day?

Does your life count for God? Does your life count for God each day? Are you first in the fight,

Standing ev-er for right? Does your life count for God each day?

for God each day?

No. 4   He Whispers Sweet Peace to my Soul

Kate Matkin Spurgeon   Virgil O. Stamps, owner, 1920   **Virgil O. Stamps**

1. Tho' sin-sick and wea-ry and sad,   And far from the longed-for goal;   'Tis Je-sus'dear voice makes me glad,
2. No mat-ter how heav-y the cares,   The bless-ed One keep-eth me whole;   And ev-'ry great bur-den He shares;
3. And when I shall reach that blest land,   I'll sing while the a-ges shall roll,   And join with the bright an-gel band—

He whispers sweet peace to my soul. He whispers sweet peace to my soul,
I'll praise Him while a-ges shall roll;
while a-ges shall roll;
I'll cling to His hand till I reach that bright land, He whispers sweet peace to my soul.
sweet peace to my soul.

No. 5 — He Arose

J. Porter Wilhite   in "Favorite Radio Songs No. 2"   Virgil O. Stamps

1. The tomb was sealed, it is re-vealed, My Lord was there in - side;
2. Yet God was there, by an - gel fair, He rolled the stone a - way;
3. Two Ma - rys true, the whole night thru, Had wait-ed near to pray;
4. He lives and reigns o'er heav'n's domains, The King of all is He;

He was se - cure, the watch was sure, He would re - main in - side.
Forth came the Lord, so says His word, Re - joice, He lives to - day.
To them Christ spake and bade them take The news to those a - way.
Tho once He died, was cru - ci - fied, He's King e - ter - nal - ly.

Chorus

But He a - rose, yes, He a - rose,
But He a - rose, yes, He a - rose,

A vic-tor, Christ a - rose; From death He came, to live a-
A vic - - tor From death He came,

rit.

gain, Tri-umph-ant o'er His foes, o'er all His foes.
to live a-gain, Tri-umph-ant o'er His foes.

No. 6   Don't Forget to Pray

Rev. L. E. Green   Virgil O. Stamps, owner   V. O. Stamps

Male voices Andante

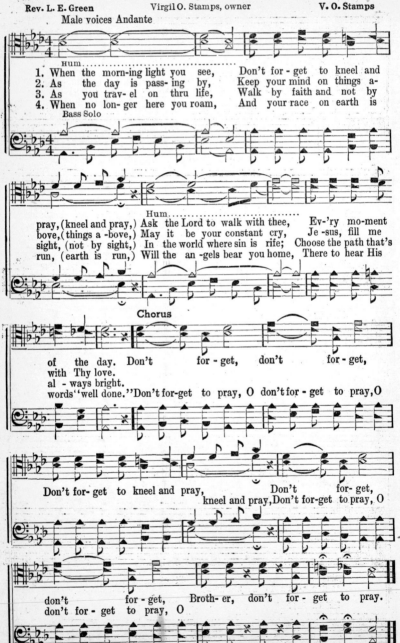

Hum......

1. When the morn-ing light you see, Don't for-get to kneel and
2. As the day is pass-ing by, Keep your mind on things a-
3. As you trav-el on thru life, Walk by faith and not by
4. When no lon-ger here you roam, And your race on earth is

Bass Solo

pray,(kneel and pray,) Ask the Lord to walk with thee, Ev-'ry mo-ment
bove,(things a-bove,) May it be your constant cry, Je-sus, fill me
sight, (not by sight,) In the world where sin is rife; Choose the path that's
run, (earth is run,) Will the an-gels bear you home, There to hear His

Hum......

Chorus

of the day. Don't for-get, don't for-get,
with Thy love.
al-ways bright.
words "well done." Don't for-get to pray, O don't for-get to pray, O

Don't for-get to kneel and pray, Don't for-get,
kneel and pray, Don't for-get to pray, O

don't for-get, Broth-er, don't for-get to pray.
don't for-get to pray, O

No. 7   Sowing the Tares

Words by a Convict in "Favorite Radio Songs No. 2" **Arr. Virgil O. Stamps**

1. Sow-ing the tares when it might have been wheat, Sow-ing of mal-ice, spite, and de-ceit; We might have sown ros-es a-mid life's sad cares, While we were so cru-el-ly sow-ing the tares.

2. Sow-ing the tares, O how dark the black sin, Min-gling a curse with life's sweet-est hymn! And heed-ing no an-guish, no pit-e-ous prayers, While we were so cru-el-ly sow-ing the tares.

3. Sow-ing the tares that will bring sor-row down, Robs of its jew-els life's fair-est crown; And turn-ing to sil-ver the once gold-en hairs, Grown whit-er and whit-er as we sowed the tares.

4. Sow-ing the tares un-der cov-er of night, Which might have been wheat, all gold-en and bright; O heart, turn to God with re-pent-ance and pray'rs, And plead His for-give-ness for sow-ing the tares.

Chorus

Sow - - ing, sow - - ing, We humbly re-pent for sow-ing the tares;
Sow-ing the tares, sow-ing the tares,

Sow - - ing, sow - - ing, We plead God's forgiveness for sowing the tares.
Sow-ing the tares, sowing the tares,

Sunlight and Shadows

Chas. W. Vaughan   Virgil O. Stamps, owner, 1919   Virgil O. Stamps

1. Fol - low - ing storm clouds, cometh the sun - light, Fol - low - ing heart-aches,
2. Brooding o'er sor - row steal- eth our com - fort, All will be well, for
3. Fol - low - ing earth life com - eth the crown-ing, In - to God's king-dom,

cometh sweet peace; So in our lives oft-times when in trou- ble, Je - sus is
God's way is best, Chastened and hum-ble we see His glo - ry, Portrayed by
af - ter a - while; See-ing the sun-light gleaming for-ev - er, Shine from our

Chorus

wait - ing to give us re -lease.
whom was giv - en the test.   Heart-aches will come, and yet there's a
Sav - ior's wel- com- ing smile.

bless- ing, Af - ter each heart ache, if we but knew, Christ is be-

hind the dark-est of storm-clouds, Sunlight will come if to Him we're true.

No. 9   The Garden of Rest

James Rowe   [Virgil O. Stamps, owner, 1924   **Virgil O. Stamps**

Duet

1. When-ev-er I'm wea-ry and sad, With Him to the gar-den I go, And soon I am feel-ing re-freshed and glad, For heav-en-ly pleas-ures o'er-flow.

2. When-ev-er my bur-den is great I walk with the Bless-ed One there, And soon from my spir-it He lifts the weight Of trou-ble or sor-row or care.

3. Some day in the gar-den at home My Lord I shall love and a-dore, And know that from Him I no more shall roam, But rest in His love ev-er-more.

1. When-ev-er I'm wea-ry and sad, With Him to the gar-den I go, For heav-en-ly pleasures o'er-flow.

Chorus

For He com-forts me and He glad-dens me, And He tells of His pre-cious love, And He lets me know that His face I shall see In the gar-den of rest a-bove.

Keep Marching All the Time

Rev. L. E. Green V. O. Stamps, owner, 1925 Virgil O. Stamps

1. If you would reach the land of end-less day, Keep marching
2. Trust in the Lord and He will lead you right,
3. By grace di-vine, a-mid the sin and strife,
4. In this vain world some day you'll cease to roam, You must keep marching

all the time;...... O nev-er faint nor fal-ter by the way,
His bless-ed word will keep your pathway bright,
The faith-ful ones will wear a crown of life,
keep marching; Some day the Lord will call the faithful home, Just

Keep marching all the time. Keep marching on,
keep marching. re-joic-ing,

REFRAIN

Keep marching on, And looking to the goal;... What-e'er be-
re-joic-ing, keep marching;

tide, trust Je-sus as your guide, And keep marching all the time ......
yes, all of the time.

His Hand Designed Them All

J. C. CROW   VIRGIL O. STAMPS

1. How great is the work of the hand di - vine Who made the stars a-
2. The birds in the trees with their tones so gay, The laugh-ing brook that
3. The fath -om -less voice of the might-y deep, The mountains great like

bove the world to shine, The beau -ti-ful flow'rs with fragrance grand Are the
winds a - long the way; The sil - ver - y moon to shine so bright, Are the
spires that up-ward leap; All won-ders of earth our eyes can trace, By His

Chorus

works of the Father's hand.   O won -der -ful world,   The
works of the Lord of Light.
wis - dom were swung in place.   filled with beau-ty rare,

glo - ry of God   The fath -om -less deep,
shin - ing ev - 'ry-where;

mountains great and small, 'Twas His hand that designed them all.......
designed them all.

WAITING THE BOATMAN.

Theme suggested to Vaughan Quartet, (Allen, Walbert, Foust and Stamps) while
waiting at Ferry on Tenn. river, midnight, July 3, 1917, near Section, Ala.

Words by Vaughan Quartet.   Music by VIRGIL O. STAMPS.

1. We are stand-ing now by the si - lent riv - er, Wait-ing the call from the
2. We are stand-ing now with the darkness 'round us, Watching the light on the
3. Hark! we hear a sound, 'tis the boatman com-ing, Hap - py are we as he

oth - er shore; We are long-ing now soon to meet our Sav-iour, Wait-ing the
oth - er shore; Man-y friends are there watching for our com-ing, Wait-ing the
dips the oar; Soon to be on board we'll be safe-ly sail - ing, Thinking of

CHORUS.

boatman to guide us o'er. Waiting the boatman, He will soon be here,
boatman to guide us o'er.
joy on the oth - er shore.   He will soon be here,

Read-y to meet Him we will have no fear,   Long-ing to see our
                     We're hap-py,

Loved ones on the shore,   Wait-ing the boatman to guide us o'er.
         We're on - ly

Drifting Away

Rev. E. A. Hoffman   Virgil O. Stamps, owner   **Virgil O. Stamps**

Drift-ing a - way,

1. Drift- ing a - way from Thy love,   Drift - ing a-
2. Drift- ing a - way from the light,   Drift - ing a-
3. Drift- ing a - way from God's grace,   Drift - ing a-

Drift-ing a - way,

way from Thy care,   Drift-ing a - way from a life of
way from the right,   Drift-ing a - way from the Cru - ci-
way from God's face,   Drift-ing a - way on the tides of

Drift - ing a - way,   Drift - ing a - way.

faith   A - way from a life of pray'r.
fied,   A - way from His bleed- ing side.
sin,   No God and no hope with - in.

Chorus

Drift-ing,   Drift-ing,
Drift-ing a - way, Drift-ing a - way, Drift-ing a - way from the love of God;

Drift-ing,   Drift-ing,   Drift-ing a-way from the cleansing blood.
Drift-ing a - way, Drift-ing a - way,

No. 14 When Dreams Come True

Mrs. Rilla Evans

Virgil O. Stamps

Melody arr. from old song of the plains

1. Some-times when I sleep in slumber so deep, A won-der-ful dream comes to
2. In rap-ture I gaze at mansions a-blaze With beau-ti-ful jew-els so
3. When dreams shall come true then heaven I'll view, That glo-ri-ous home of the

me; A vis-ion so bright that gives me de - light, The glo-ries of
rare, And lo! I be-hold the streets of pure gold And beau-ty be-
soul; With an - gels I'll sing and praise my dear King, While a - ges e-

Chorus

heav-en I'll see. Sav - ior I'll meet, Sav-ior I'll meet,
yond all com-pare.
ter - nal shall roll. My Sav - ior I'll meet..... ...... And

Loved ones I'll greet, my loved ones I'll greet, Some day when my dreams come true; That
loved ones I'll greet,.......... come true;

wonderful land, with mansions so grand, I'll see when my dreams all come true.

No. 15   Sometime

R. B. Taylor   Virgil O. Stamps, owner, 1926   Virgil O. Stamps

1. Sometime this life...... will all be o'er,...... My earthly strife........
2. Sometime my Lord.... will call, I know,..... And if I am..........
3. Sometime, someday.... I hope to see....... My Sav-ior dear,........
4. Sometime His voice.... will call to you,..... Will you be wait-........

will be no more,.......... Then on the wings....... of love I'll
pre-pared to go,............ Then by His grace....... my life made
who died for me,............ And at His feet........ my sheaves lay
ing read-y too?.......... No long-er from......... your Sav-ior

D. S.—*When all earth's toils........ have past a-*
FINE

fly,........Where angels sing .... in realms on high..........
pure,...... 'Twill make my faith........ and call-ing sure..........
down,...... And there re-ceive........ a shin-ing crown..........
stray,...... But give your heart ...... to Him to - day..........

way, ... And dwell in that.......... e - ter - nal day...........

CHORUS

Sometime, sometime, (Sometime, sometime,) some hap-py time, (some hap-py time,)

D. S.

My soul shall reach (My soul shall reach) that sun-ny clime; (that sun - ny clime;)

Let me Draw Nearer to Thee

Rev. Johnson Oatman, Jr.   Virgil O. Stamps, owner   Virgil O. Stamps

Very slow

Hum.......

1. Dear Sav-ior, I'm walk-ing too far from Thy side, Let me draw near-er to
2. I've heard Thy voice call-ing to fol-low, dear Lord,
3. Thy face and Thy form I more clear-ly would see,
4. And when the last riv-er some day I be-hold, Let me draw

Thee;   Re - mov-ing each bit of self seek - ing and pride,
To walk at a dis-tance I can - not af - ford,
Thy friend and Thy lov - ing com-pan - ion to be,
near - er to Thee; Un-til I shall en - ter the streets of pure gold,

Hum.......

Chorus

Let me draw near-er to Thee.   Near - er,
Let me draw near-er to Thee. Near-er and near-er, still

near - er to Thee, Let me draw near-er, dear Sav-ior, to Thee, Near -
to Thee,   Near-er and

rit.

er,   near - er to Thee, Let me draw near - er to Thee.
near-er, still   Let me draw near-er to Thee.

No. 17   Won't We Be Happy?

D. C. and J. R. B., Jr.   Denver Crumpler and V. O. S.

1. Here we have sor-row, Pain, grief and care; When dawns that mor-row,
2. Here joy is fleet-ing, Lasts but a day; Soon we'll be greet-ing,
3. Here we have weep-ing, Loved ones have gone; No storms are sweep-ing,

Chorus faster

No tri-als there.
Friends o'er the way. O won't we be so hap-py in heav-en, When we
Where morn shall dawn.

all get there? We'll meet many friends and loved ones, Now won't that be joy be-

yond compare? There will be no heart-ache nor sor-row, Not an-y bur-dens to

bear, We'll sing to the King, we'll make hallelujahs ring, When we all get there.

Look For Me, For I'll Be There

V. O. S.

Virgil O. Stamps, owner

Virgil O. Stamps

1. When you reach your home in glory,　　Free from ev-'ry toil and care,
2. Christ, the Lord, has long been with me,　　Shielding me from ev-'ry snare;
3. Won't it be a hap py meet-ing,　　When you meet your loved ones there
4. Won't there be a joy-ous sing-ing,　　In that home so bright and fair,
1. When you reach your home, home in glo-ry,

Where the saved shall dwell for-ev-er,　　You may look for me, for I'll
He will lead me safe to heav en,　　You may look for me, for I'll
In the home of end-less glo-ry?　　You may look for me, for I'll
When the heav'nly choir as-sem-bles?　　You may look for me, for I'll
Where the saved shall dwell, dwell, for-ev-er,

CHORUS

be there....　Look for me, (Oh, look for me,) Look for me, (For I'll be there;)

You will find me with the an-gels fair, Look for me,
You will find me with the angels fair,　　Oh, look for me,

Look for me,　　Don't for-get to look for me up there.
For I'll be there; Don't for-get to look for me up there.

Cling to the Cross

V. O. Stamps, owner,

Rev. Johnson Oatman, Jr.   Virgil O. Stamps

1. At your feet ev-'ry moment, my brother, Do the bil-lows of life
2. There are ma-ny a-round you now sinking, Those dear lives would you pre-
3. Look, the life-boat is com-ing from heav-en, See its ban-ner of white

foam and toss?... Still for you there's a way to es-cape them, You must
vent from loss?... Reach one hand to them, but with the oth-er You must
proud-ly toss;... But un-til it has anchored beneath you, You must

cling, cling, cling to the cross.

CHORUS

You must cling, cling, cling to the old rugged cross,

cross,......

You must cling, cling, cling to the cross;........ No trouble can down you, no
cross, the rugged cross;

bil-low can drown you, If you cling, cling, cling to the cross.........
old rug-ged cross.

I Believe It All

V. O. Stamps, owner. 1925

James Rowe Virgil O. Stamps

1. In these lat - ter days ma - ny calls are heard From the doubters who
2. Ma-ny pas - sag - es they be - gin to doubt, Want this page and that
3. Blessed book di - vine, it shall al - ways be God's e - ter - nal word,

want to change God's word; But in vain to me for sup-port they call,
to be tak - en out; But as naught their words on my spir - it fall,
breathing love for me; I shall trust its light and I shall not fall;

CHORUS

For I'm glad to say, "I be-lieve it all."
For, with all my heart, I be-lieve it all. I be-lieve it all, ev - 'ry
Glo - ry be to God! I be-lieve it all.

word and line; I be-lieve it all, bless-ed book di-vine; And I know no

rit.

harm shall His Word befall; Praise and bless His name, I be - lieve it all!

The Cross On the Hill

Herbert Buffum **Virgil O. Stamps**

1. In the days long a-go, there in an-guish and woe, There were those whose ap-peal had been lost; And stern jus-tice de-creed they must die for their deed, So they put them to death on a cross.

2. There were cross-es on plains with their quo-ta of pains, Man-y vic-tims re-mained there un-til Gone each quiv-er-ing breath, but no oth-er man's death Meant so much as that cross on the hill.

3. Just a slight roll-ing hill, with a task to ful-fill, And a plain, com-mon cross from a tree; But they're each glo-ri-fied thru the God-man who died That the whole world from sin might go free.

Fine

D.S.—And the whole world has hope thru that pray'r.

Chorus

O the cross on the hill, rug-ged cross on the hill, 'Twas our bridge o'er the gulf of de-spair; Je-sus will-ing-ly died, "O for-give them" He cried,

D.S.

Nothing in Heaven but Love

Walter E. Edmiaston   Virgil O. Stamps

1. If you can't get a-long with your fel-low-man, What will you
2. If you lie, cheat or steal, or live false-ly now, You can-not
3. If you can-not spread peace, joy and glad-ness share, You will not

do in heav-en? Those who go there must live by the Bi-ble plan,
get to heav-en; Ev-'ry soul in that land to God's will must bow,
be in heav-en; For the saints live in peace in that home up there,

CHORUS

There's nothing in heav'n but love.... There's nothing in heav'n but love,....
true love,

There's noth-ing in heav'n but love;........ O if you "back bite" here
O no cheat-er down here
there's nothing but love; O if you hate while here

you'll have no place there, There's nothing in heav'n but love..........
will be found up there,
you will not go there,
God's love.

No. 23   When All of God's Singers Get Home

Luther G. Presley   Copyright, 1937, by Stamps-Baxter Music Co.,
Cho. V. O. S.   in "Starlit Crown"   Virgil O. Stamps

1. What a song of de-light in that ci-ty so bright Will be waft-ed 'neath
2. As we sing here on earth, songs of sad-ness or mirth, 'Tis a fore-taste of
3. Hav-ing o-ver-come sin, "hal-le-lu-jah a-men" Will be heard in that

heav-en's fair dome, How the ransomed will raise hap-py songs in His praise,
rap-ture to come; But our joy can't com-pare with the glo-ry up there,
land o'er the foam, Ev-'ry heart will be light and each face will be bright,

Chorus

When all of God's singers get home. When all of God's singers get home,
     When all of God's singers get home,

Where nev-er a sor-row will come;   There'll be "no
     or heart-aches will come;   There'll be no

place like home,"   When all of God's sing-ers get home.
place like heav-en my home,   God's singers get home.

No. 24   My Soul Will Never Die

Mrs. Rilla Evans   Virgil O. Stamps

1. Tho' storms so fierce..... a-round me roll,..... They cannot harm.....
2. All flesh and blood...... will pass a-way..... And change to dust.....
3. When death shall come.... for me some day,.....My soul shall rise.....

my trust-ing soul; (my trusting soul;) On Je-sus Christ...... I will re-
till judgment day, (till judgment day,)The word of God..... we can't de-
and soar a-way (and soar a-way) To find a place........ be-yond the

D. S.—*And be at rest..........with all the*

FINE

ly,.......... I know my soul........ will nev-er die. (will nev-er die.)
ny,.......... The soul of man........ will nev-er die. (will nev-er die.)
sky,....... Where it will rest........ and nev-er die. (and nev-er die.)

blest,....... My soul will live..........and nev-er die. (and nev-er die.)

CHORUS

This soul of mine............. will nev-er die,............ .
This soul of mine   will nev-er die,

D. S.

It will re-turn........ to God on high,............
It will re-turn   to God on high,

When I Lay My Burdens Down

A. M. Newbill

Owned by the authors, 1929

Stamps, Yandell and Baxter

1. There's a land of beau-ty and pure de-light, It is a-cross the riv - er
2. I'll be with the ran-somed ones o-ver there, Sharing their joy and glo-ry,
3. Some sweet day, I know that it can't be long, I shall join in the sing-ing

where there will be no night; There I'll wear a beau-ti-ful gold-en crown,
liv - ing with an - gels fair; I'll meet saints of old, who have won re-nown,
with all the blood-bought throng; I'll have joy that waves of the sea can't drown,

REFRAIN

When I lay my heav - y bur - dens down. When I
When in His presence there I

lay all my burdens down, I'll re - ceive a bright golden crown;
lay all my burdens down, I shall receive from Him a beau-ti-ful golden crown;

No more sorrow, never a sigh or frown, When I lay my heav-y bur-dens down.

Jesus is My King

Copyright, 1926, by Virgil O. Stamps

Winifred O. Webster   Virgil O. Stamps

1. Is your life one gladsome day? Are flowers blooming round you all the way?
2. Are your skies all dark and drear? And is there in your heart no song of cheer?
3. Do you glimpse life's Western sun, In hope to hear, at last, your Lord's "Well done?"

Are your friends all tried and true? Then tell them what the Savior means to you.
Then with faith still strong and true, Just tell the world what Jesus means to you.
Then you'll find 'tis joy most true To tell the world what Jesus is to you.

REFRAIN.

Peace and sweet con-tent-ment on life's wea-ry mile, Just do-ing what He

bids me with a joy-ous smile; Bear-ing high His stand-ard

as I glad-ly sing, That all the world may know that Je-sus is my King.

(For 1927 Book)

O Prince of Peace

Noah White   Virgil O. Stamps

1. O Prince of Peace,........ the tem-pest roars,........ Our bark is tossed,...... we are dis-tressed;...... We can-not long - - - - er trust our oars,............

2. O Prince of Peace,........ all else has failed,........ Our wis-est men........ have done their best;........ But naught for last - - - - ing peace a - vailed,.........

3. O Prince of Peace,........ Thy sub-jects wait,........ And long for Thee........ when foes mo-lest;........ Throw o-pen soon........ the pearl - y gate,........ ...Come Thou O Prince of Peace in right-eous-ness............

D.S.—Come reign o'er us........

Come and give us rest. **Fine**

Chorus

O Prince of Peace,   sweet Prince of Peace,
O Prince of Peace,   sweet Prince of Peace,

D.S.

Come quick-ly, grant   our heart's re-quest;
Come quick-ly, grant   our fond re-quest;

Redemption's Melody

Rev. B. B. Edmiaston Copyright, 1931, by V. O. Stamps **Virgil O. Stamps**

1. In my heart I have a song of glad-ness, Mel - o - dy of ev - er-
2. I re - joice to sing this hap - py car - ol, For it turns life's sor-rows
3. Here I'll sing it till this life is end - ed, Praising Christ, my Sav-ior,

last-ing love; I re-ceived it when I trust-ed Je - sus, 'Tis a son - net
in - to joy; 'Tis the song of fall - en man's redemption, Glorious theme that
o'er and o'er; Then I'll sing it with a voice that's perfect, 'Round the great white

CHORUS

from the world a-bove. My Lord gave this pre-cious song to me,
angel's tongues employ.
throne for-ev-er-more. Je - sus gave this precious song to me,

With joy I'll sing, sing it o'er and o'er, Redemption's blood-bought
Glad - ly I will sing it o'er and o'er,

mel - o - dy, Je-sus bro't it, an-gels taught it, saints will sing it ev - er-more.

No. 29   When I Play on My Harp of Gold

Rev. Johnson Oatman, Jr.   Copyright, 1926, by V. O. Stamps   Virgil O. Stamps

1. Far a-way past the shad-ows of night is a land, Whose in-
hab-i-tants nev-er grow old, And in sweet con-tem-pla-tion I
oft-en de-light, Thinking o-ver my joys in that cit-y so bright,

2. There will ga-ther to lis-ten to me while I play, All the
saints and the an-gels I'm told, As my mu-sic rolls out o-ver
pearl gate and wall, I will play as young Dav-id once played be-fore Saul,

3. There in glo-ry and pow-er up-on His white throne, I my
Sa-vior and King shall be-hold, Then His prais-es in tones that will
roll rich and clear, I will sing as I've nev-er been a-ble to here,

D. S.—*I will sweep all its strings in that cit-y so fair, And my song will ring out on the ra-ri-fied air,*

FINE CHORUS

When I play on my harp of gold. When I play on my harp, on my
When I play on my

harp of pure gold—I will sing the sweet sto-ry that nev-er grows old;
harp of gold,

D. S.

At the Post of Duty

Don Hooper   V. O. Stamps, owner, 1925   Virgil O. Stamps

1. At the post of du-ty, work-ing for the crown, Winning souls for Je-sus,
2. At the post of du-ty, till the Sav-ior comes, Home with Him to gather
3. At the post of du-ty, work will soon be o'er, All the faith-ful ones we'll

who for us came down; From His home in glo-ry, that we might be free;
all His chos-en ones; Songs of praise keep singing, to the ho-ly Dove,
meet on that blest shore; Then we'll sing to-geth-er, voic-ing there His praise,

FINE   CHORUS

Hap-py in His love for-ev-er let us be. At the post of du-ty,
He who keeps us free and saves us by His love.
'Round the throne for-ev-er, thru unnumbered days. At the post of du-ty,

D.S.—*Onward, upward striving, working for the crown.*

heed-ing His command, March-ing home to glo-ry, with Him
heed-ing His command, Marching home to glo-ry, with Him hand in

D. S.

hand in hand; Win-ning souls for Je-sus, till life's sun goes down,
hand; Winning souls for Je-sus, till life's sun goes down,

You Will Reap What You Sow

N. W. ALLPHIN COPYRIGHT, 1938 BY V. O. STAMPS VIRGIL O. STAMPS

1. Broth-er, what of the seed you are sow - ing, As a-long (As a-long)
2. Do you sow to the flesh or the spir - it, As you tread (As you tread)
3. Thot's and words for a har-vest you're sow-ing, In - to deeds (In-to deeds)
4. Is your sow-ing for glo - ry and hon - or? Will it be (Will it be)

the way you go? (the way you go?) You should choose them with carefulness,
this vale be-low? (this vale be-low?) Do you hope end-less joys to in-
they'll sure-ly grow; (they'll surely grow;) Either bless-ings or curs - es be-
for weal or woe? (for weal or woe?) By and by when your har-vest you

Chorus

know-ing,
her - it? You shall reap (You shall reap) just what you sow. You shall reap......
stow - ing,   You shall reap
gar - ner,

what you sow,......You shall reap..... just what you sow;..... Oh, "be
what you sow,   You shall reap   what you sow;

not deceived, for God is not mocked," You shall reap ...just what you sow.
                                        You shall reap just what you sow.

I'm Going On

J. R. Baxter, Jr. Ref. V. O. S. Virgil O. Stamps

Not fast

1. I've found the straight and narrow way That ends some golden dawn, Till I shall
2. The path grows brighter all the time, I'm clos - er to Him drawn; I feel se -
3. I'm fac - ing now the glo - ry-land Where many friends have gone, They won't have

see the gates swing o - pen, With my Lord I am go - ing on.
cure while in His keep-ing,
long to wait my com-ing, I am go - ing on........

REFRAIN *Faster*

I'm go-ing on,.......... I'm go-ing on,........... I've left the
I'm go - ing on,.......... I'm go- ing on,

sin - ful world be-hind; Since Christ has saved my soul His love-waves o'er me
I'm go-ing on, I'm go-ing

roll, I do not dread the sep - a - rat - ing time.
on, I do not dread the sep - a - rat - ing time..............

Let Me Live Close to Thee

J. R. Baxter, Jr.   Copyright, 1927, V. O. Stamps   Virgil O. Stamps

1. In Thy field I would yield sick-les brave and true, In the fight for the right
2. Not the crown nor re-nown that the world might see, I would work, nev-er shirk,
3. Help me bear and to share some poor pilgrim's load, Be my friend to the end

I would dare and do, Spend my days in Thy praise all the journey thru, Let me
bless-ed Lord, for Thee, But to know where I go that my soul is free, Let me
or the toilsome road, I would sing to my King in the soul's a-bode, Let me

Chorus

live close to Thee each day.   Let me live   close to Thee,
Let me live   close to Thee,   Take my

Guide me all a - long the way;   Let me live
hand, dear Lord, and guide me all a-long the rug-ged way; O let me live

close to Thee,   Let me walk   close to Thee each day.
close to Thee,   Let me walk and talk with Thee, dear Lord, each day.

Anchored on the Rock

B. W. Pirtle   Copyright, 1929, by V. O. Stamps   Virgil O. Stamps

Alto prominent

1. On Je-sus my Sav-ior I'll ev-er re-ly, For He is my help-er and
2. I'll nev-er forsake Him nor turn Him away, But on this great rock I am
3. Come anchor your soul on the rock that's secure, Thru ages 'twill stand and for-

al-ways is nigh; To shield me from dan-ger and com-fort my soul, O
anchored to stay; His love is so boundless, so full and so free, For-
ev-er en-dure; He'll shield you from dan-ger, no mat-ter how great, And

REFRAIN

He is more precious than sil-ver or gold. I'm anchored, anchored,
ev-er He's shielding and com-fort-ing me.
some day you'll share that e-ter-nal es-tate. I'm anchored, yes, anchored on

safe on the rock, Anchored, anchored, free from all shock; He shields me from
Je-sus the rock, And He can withstand ev'ry tempest and shock;

dan-ger and comforts my soul, When storm clouds would gather and over me roll.

No. 35 When They Ring Those Welcome Bells

Copyright, 1935, by The Stamps-Baxter Music Co.,
in "Harbor Bells No. 4"

Thomas Ramsey

Virgil O. Stamps

1. There's a land of E-den just o'er the sea, Where the Lamb of God all
2. I can hear the sing-ing of heav-en's choir, Soft-ly on my ear the
3. Soon I'll join the num-ber gone on be-fore, Bright-ly now this hope with-

gloom dis-pels; There with friends and loved ones I soon shall be When
mu-sic swells; Soon I shall be sing-ing just like they are
in me dwells; Trou-bles will be o-ver on that glad shore When they

CHORUS

they ring those wel-come bells. When they ring the bells of
ring those wel-come bells.... Some morning

heav-en .... Where the Ho-ly Spir-it dwells,..........
bells of heav-en the Spir-it dwells, I'll

Put on my robe and my golden crown When they ring those welcome bells.
When they ring those welcome bells, welcome bells.

Are You Living Right?
STOP! AND THINK!

Don Hooper · Copyright, 1929, by V. O. Stamps · Virgil O. Stamps

1. As you press along the way there's a question that will pay: Are you liv-ing right each day? Are you free from doubt and sin, does His love abide within? Are you liv-ing right each day?
2. Do you help the downcast here when their way is dark and drear? Are you liv-ing right each day? Do you point them home a-bove, telling of the Savior's love? Are you liv-ing right each day?
3. Do you humbly kneel and pray to the Father ev'ry day? Are you liv-ing right each day? Peace and par-don do you claim in the blessed Savior's name? Are you liv-ing right each day?

CHORUS

In the bless-ed Master's sight, Are you liv-ing right?.... Do you walk the nar-row way? Do you tell His boundless love, On your way a-bove? each day?

In the Mas-ter's sight, Are you al-ways living right? Do you tell His love,.... On your way a-bove? Are you liv-ing right each day?

I Will Meet You There

Arr. V. O. S. V. O. Stamps, owner, 1925 Arr. by Virgil O. Stamps

1. There's a land that is fair-er than day, I will meet you o-ver
2. We shall sing on that beau-ti-ful shore, I will meet you o-ver
3. With our boun-ti-ful Fa-ther a-bove, I will meet you o-ver

there some day; Where our Fa-ther waits o-ver the way, I will
there some day; And our spir-its shall sor-row no more, I will
there some day; In a home filled with rap-ture and love, I will

CHORUS

meet you o-ver there some day. I will meet you o-ver there in the

morn - - ing, I will meet you with the an-gels fair; In the
morning, in the morning,

land that is fair-er than day, I will meet you, I will meet you there......
o - ver there.

Honor Him With Praise

N. W. Allphin

Virgil O. Stamps

1. Songs of glad-ness gath-er we now to sing, Joy-ful-ly our trib-ute of
2. Sing, ye ransomed, praise Him with heart and voice, Make His service willing-ly
3. Sing, keep singing, let-ting His praise abound, Till His name is honored the

praise we bring; Laud we Him whom heavenly hosts adore, Honor be unto His name,
here your choice; Let each soul melodious praise out-pour, Until the ech-oes resound
world around; Worship Him whose marvelous love and grace Offers salvation from sin,

CHORUS

now and for-ev-er more! Sing the sto-o-ry,
on the e-ter-nal shore!
free-ly to all our race! Sing of the Savior's glory, shouting abroad the story,

Maj-es-ty, pow'r and might for-ev-er to Him be-long; Give Him
Give Him, in song and story,

glo-o-ry, Bright-en the world with gladsome song! . . . .
boun-ti-ful praise and glo-ry, sweet song!

No. 39   When the Saints Go Marching In

Arr. Copyright, 1937, by The Stamps-Baxter Music Co.,
in "Starlit Crown"

By LUTHER G. PRESLEY   Arr. VIRGIL O. STAMPS

1. I'm just a wea-ry pil-grim, Plod-ding thru this world of sin;
2. My fa-ther loved the Sav-ior, What a sol-dier he had been!
3. And mo-ther, may God bless her, I can see her now, as then;
4. Up there I'll see the Sav-ior Who re-deemed my soul from sin,

Get-ting read-y for that ci-ty
But his steps will be more stead-y
With a robe of white a-round her
With ex-tend-ed hands He'll greet me

When the saints go march-ing in.
Saints go march-ing

Chorus

When the saints go marching in, When the saints go
When the saints marching in, Saints go

march-ing in; Lord I want to be in that
march-ing go marching in O

number When the saints go march-ing in.
that number, Saints go march-ing go marching in.

count-less number,

No. 40   Crown the Savior Here

Rev. Johnson Oatman, Jr.   Copyright, 1928, by V. O. Stamps   Virgil O. Stamps

1. When Christians meet together, how oft we talk and sing A-bout the time we'll
gath - er to crown the Sav-ior king; But there's a truth, my broth-er, that
ought to be made clear, If we would crown Him yon-der, He first must be crowned here.

2. We'll nev-er crown the Savior a-bove yon vaulted dome Un-less His cor - o-
na-tion takes place with-in each home; If we with those who crown Him in
heav-en would ap-pear, We first must yield the scepter to Je-sus while we're here.

3. If we are true to Je-sus in thot and word and deed, No pub-lic cer-e-
mo - ny of crown-ing will He need; For if our lives are right-eous, our
ev - 'ry ac-tion now Will help to crown with glo-ry our blessed Savior's brow.

D. S.—*we'll not help to crown Him in that celestial sphere, Till King of our affections we all have crowned Him here.*

REFRAIN

O yes, we want to crown Him who has our sins for-giv'n, O
yes, we want to crown Him with - in the halls of heav'n; But

We want to crown the One who has our sins forgiv'n, We
want to crown our Lord with - in the halls of heav'n; But

Have a Friend Like Mine

James Rowe   Virgil O. Stamps

1. Why be lone-ly, sad and drear-y And from day to day re-pine?
2. Why in darkness still be liv-ing Where the hordes of sin af-fright?
3. Why the fu-ture still be dreading? He would take thy fear a-way,
4. Why be downward ev-er go-ing? Why not cease in sin to roam?

Why be al-ways worn and wea-ry, Why not have a Friend like mine?
To the Lord thy heart be giv-ing, He will give you peace and light.
On thy soul His brightness shedding, He would turn thy night to day.
Have thy heart with praise o'er-flowing, Let my Sav-ior guide thee home.

CHORUS *Faster*

Why not have a Friend like mine, One whose love is so di-vine? Why be sad when I re-joice, Why not have a Friend like mine?

Why not have a Friend like mine, ... One whose love is so di-vine? .... Why be lone and sad when I'm re-joic-ing? Why not have a Friend like mine? ....

Singing on the Way

Rev. L. E. Green Copyright, 1928, by V. O. Stamps Virgil O. Stamps

1. I praise the Lord for saving grace, Sing-ing on the way to glo-ry-land;
2. I'm on the way the prophets went, Sing ing on the way to glo-ry-land;
3. O come, dear friends and go with me, Sing-ing on the way to glo-ry-land;
4. I'm walking in the way called straight, Sing-ing on the way to glo-ry-land;

By faith I'll run the pil-grim race, Singing on the way to glo-ry-land.
I have sweet peace and soul content, Singing on the way to glo-ry-land.
And day by day more hap-py be, Singing on the way to glo-ry-land.
Some day I'll reach the pearly gate, Singing on the way to glo-ry-land.

REFRAIN

Sing-ing on the way, (I am) singing on the way, (walking) With the blood-washed
band; (the blood-washed band, yes, I am) Sing-ing on the way, (I am)
sing-ing on the way, (O I'm) Sing-ing on the way to glo-ry-land.

No. 43   Which Will You Choose?

Deut. 30: 19

Copright, 1928, by V. O. Stamps

V. O. S.

Virgil O. Stamps

Mixed Quartet

1. God sets before you life and death, my friend, Think well be-
2. There is a way that seemeth right to man, The end there-
3. The broad way leads to pleasures here be-low, But soon they

1. God sets before you life and death, my friend, Think well

fore you choose; (before you choose;) The time will come when earthly
of is death; (the end is death;) Then there's a way that leads to
all must end; (they all must end;) The oth - er leads where joys for-
be-fore you choose; (be-fore you choose;) The time will come when

D. S.—*God sets before you life and*

FINE

things must end, God's mer - cy don't re-fuse. (do not re-fuse.)
glo - ry - land, Choose now while you have breath. (while you have breath.)
ev - er flow, Which will you choose, my friend? (my sin-ner friend?)
earthly things must end, God's mer-cy don't re-fuse.......

death, my friend, Which will you choose to-day? (which choose to-day?)

CHORUS

Which will you choose?   Which will you choose?
Which will you choose to - day?.................

Which will you choose?   Which will you choose?
Which will you choose to - day?.................

D. S.

Joy

Rev. B. B. Edmiaston   Virgil O. Stamps

1. There is won-der-ful joy in serv-ing the Lord, There is pleas-ure unknown out-side of His love; There is glad-ness supreme in trust-ing His word, Joy that lifts up the life t'ward heav-en a-bove.

2. There is rap-tur-ous joy in seek-ing the lost, In re-peat-ing the old, old sto-ry of love; In re-view-ing to men the in-fi-nite cost, For the Fa-ther to send His Son from a-bove.

3. There is soul-thrill-ing joy when one is made whole, When he turns from his sin, no lon-ger to roam; Yes, the an-gels a-bove re-joice when a soul, That's redeemed by the blood, re-pent-ing, comes home.

CHORUS

Joy, ... there is won-der-ful joy, Joy, joy, joy in serv-ing the Lord, Sor - rows no lon-ger an-noy,

joy, joy   Great joy and glad-ness   The pangs of sor-row no

Joy

Souls who trust God's word, God's word, How sweet...... is the
The souls who trust Je - ho - vah's word, how sweet

mes-sage of love, Bro't to us from heav-en a - bove, Re-
Bro't to lost mor - tals

joice sing, tell it a-gain, There is joy, joy, joy......
and yes, won - der - ful joy.

No. 45   I'll Live For Him

R. E. Hudson   C. R. Dunbar

1. My life, my love I give to Thee, Thou Lamb of God who died for me;
2. I now be-lieve Thou dost re-ceive, For Thou hast died that I might live;
3. O Thou who died on Cal - va - ry, To save my soul and make me free,

CHO.—I'll live for Him who died for me, How hap-py then my life shall be!

D. C. for chorus

O may I ev - er faith-ful be, My Sav - ior and my God!
And now henceforth I'll trust in Thee, My Sav - ior and my God!
I'll con - se - crate my life to Thee, My Sav - ior and my God!

I'll live for Him who died for me, My Sav - ior and my God!

There's Glory There.

Don Hopper.   V. O. Stamps, owner, 1921.   Virgil O. Stamps.

1. We are prom-ised a home in glo - ry, Hap-py home with the
2. In that home-land of fade-less beau-ty, Is a man-sion so
3. When in safe - ty we've reached that cit - y, We shall sing with the
4. O, that glad time is draw-ing near - er, When we'll meet there to

an - gels fair; Where the saved of the earth will greet us, O, there's
bright and fair; Where the ransomed shall rest for - ev - er, Free from
hosts up there; Prais-ing Je - sus, the match-less Sav - iour, Who was
part no more; But with saints 'round the throne for-ev - er, We will

CHORUS.

won - der-ful glo - ry there.   O,   there's glo - ry, glo-ry there,
sor - row and free from care.
slain all our sins to bear.
sing on the gold - en shore.   O, there is glo - ry, there's glo - ry there,

In that blest home, that home so fair; Glo - ry be to His name, There we'll
In that home so fair; . . . .

ev - er pro-claim, For there's glo - ry, glo - ry, glo - ry three.
end-less won-der - ful

I Need Jesus Every Day

James Rowe   V. O. Stamps, owner, 1926   V. O. Stamps

1. With sins for-giv-en I'm fac-ing Heav-en, And nev-er-more in-
2. I'll praise for-ev-er my bless-ed Sav-ior, And glad-ly serve Him
3. For Je-sus liv-ing, my best I'm giv-ing, And shall till I am
4. Till safe in glo-ry I'll tell His sto-ry, And how He took my

tend to stray; To guide and cheer me, my Lord is near me, Be-
where I may; So He will guide me, when foes be-tide me, Be-
called a-way; I'll nev-er leave Him, or slight or grieve Him, Be-
sins a-way; Then praise Him ev-er be-side the riv-er, Be-

CHORUS

cause I need Him ev-'ry day. Oh, yes, I need Him ev'ry day, ...
ev-'ry day,

And He needs me a-long the way; .... We stay to-geth-er in
a-long the way;

ev-'ry kind of weather, And help each oth-er ev-'ry day.

When He Comes Back Again

Luther G. Presley   Virgil O. Stamps

1. When Je-sus came from glo-ry to die for fal-len man, By His own
2. We know not when He's coming in all His glory bright, He tells us
3. He tells us of the beau-ty around the Father's throne, Of man-sions

will He did ful-fill sal - va-tion's plan; And when He went to heaven, His
we must read-y be at noon or night; And only those who love Him with
fair He did pre-pare for all His own; We cannot hope to meet Him with

own stood weeping then, But in His word He tells us He's com-ing back a-gain.
joy can greet Him then, Will Jesus find you ready when He comes back a-gain?
garments stained with sin, What then will be your record when He comes back again?

CHORUS

Our Lord ..... is sure-ly com-ing, It won't be ver-y long,   We'll
          is sure - ly   not long, We'll

see. ..... Him in His glo - ry, and sing ..... the triumph song,
see Him in   His   the tri - umph song, glad song,

When He Comes Back Again

Maj - - es - ty and pow - er to rule the hearts of men,
In His maj - es - ty and of men,

In bright array, some blessed day, He's com-ing back a - gain...........
com - ing back a - gain.

No. 49   Love Found a Way For Me

J. R. B., Jr.   Copyright, 1927, by J. R. Baxter, Jr.   J. R. Baxter, Jr.

1. When I was lost in sin and disgrace, Love   found a way for me;
2. Once I was bound by fetters of shame,
3. 'Twas all because my God loved me so, Wonderful love found a way for me;

Now I can find in heaven my place, Love   found a way for me.
Now I am free, O praise His dear name,
Now I can sing as homeward I go, Won-der-ful love found a way for me.

D. S.–"Once I was blind but now I can see," Love   found a way for me.

REFRAIN

Love   found a way for me, Love   found a way for me;
Won-der-ful love   Won-der-ful love

No. 50 Launch Out on the Sea of God's Love

Rev. B. B. Edmiaston   Copyright, 1930, by V. O. Stamps   Virgil O. Stamps

1. Dear friend, are you trust-ing the Sav-ior to-day, Ac-cept-ing His
2. True faith in Him, tho' it is small, will re-move The mountains of
3. O trust not in self, but re-ly on the Lord, With heart set on

prom-is-es sweet; Is faith tak-ing hold of His word to o-bey,
doubt and of sin; By work-ing for Je-sus your faith you will prove,
things up a-bove; Be-liev-ing each prom-ise contained in His word,

CHORUS

In bless-ed as-sur-ance com-plete? Launch out to-day,
And, thru Him, the vic-to-ry win.
Launch out on the sea of God's love. Launch out.......... on the

out on the sea, On the sea of God's love,
sea,.......... Launch out on the sea of God's love,.......... The

Faith of His saints, faith of His saints, Mountains will move,
faith.......... of His saints,.......... The moun - - - tains will

Launch Out on the Sea of God's Love

mourtains will move; Launch out to-day, out on the sea,
move; .... Launch out .... on the sea, ... Launch

And God's prom-is-es prove, Doubt Him no more,
out and the prom-is-es prove, ... O doubt... ...... Him no

doubt Him no more, Launch out on the sea of God's love..........
more, ... out on the sea of God's love.

No. 51   He Knows

G. W. Lyon

With expression

1. He knows the bit-ter, wea-ry way, The end-less strivings day by day,
2. He knows how hard the fight has been, The clouds that come our lives between,
3. He knows when faint and worn we sink, How deep the pain, how near the brink
4. He knows! O tho't so full of bliss! For tho' on earth our joys we miss,

Hum..

The souls that weep, the souls that pray, He knows,   He knows.
The wounds the world has nev-er seen,
Of dark de-spair, we pause and shrink,
We still can bear it feel-ing this,   He knows,   He knows.

Follow, Follow Me

Geo. O. Webster   Copyright, 1926, by V. O. Stamps   Virgil O. Stamps

1. A call we hear o'er hill and vale re-sound-ing, 'Tis ring-ing
2. A call we hear, a voice di - vine is plead-ing, Give list-'ning
3. A call we hear, oh, hear with-out de - lay-ing, While He is

clear on ev - 'ry land and sea: The ac - cents fall, with
ear, for love is seek - ing thee; It comes to all, from
near, with par - don full and free, Oh, heed His call, while

love and grace a-bound-ing, The Sav-ior's call: "Come, fol - low me."
One whose heart is bleed-ing, The Sav-ior's call: "Come, fol - low me."
still in love He's say-ing To one and all: "Come, fol - low me."

CHORUS

Fol-low, fol - low, fol - low me! Fol-low, fol - low,
fol-low, fol - low me!

fol - low me! Hear the Savior's voice entreating, O'er and o'er in
fol-low, fol-low me!

love re-peat-ing: Fol-low, won't you fol-low, Come and fol-low me!

No. 53 **Whiter Than Snow**

(HOLY NIGHT)

James Nicholson

Franz Gruber
Arr. V. O. Stamps

1. Lord Je-sus, I long to be per-fect-ly whole; I want Thee for-
2. Lord Je-sus, look down from Thy throne in the skies, And help me to
3. Lord Je-sus, Thou see-est I pa-tient-ly wait, Come now, and with-

ev - er to live in my soul; Break down ev-'ry i-dol, cast
make a com-plete sac-ri-fice; I give up my-self, and what-
in me a new heart cre-ate; To those who have sought Thee Thou

out ev-'ry foe;
ev - er I know; } Now wash me and I shall be whit-er than snow,
nev - er saidst "No,"

rit.

Wash me and I shall be whit-er than snow, I shall be whit-er than snow.

On the Cross

Virgil O. Stamps

1. On the rug-ged cross, on the cru-el cross, Je-sus gave His life for men;
2. Look and see Him now, there on Calv'ry's brow, With the spear thrust in His side;
3. 'Twas for you and me that the ag-o-ny Of the cross by Christ was borne;
4. Sin-ner far a-way from the Lord to-day, Come to Him be-fore too late;

He was cru-ci-fied, free-ly bled and died, Just to save our souls from sin.
See the crown of thorns, which His brow adorns, As He free-ly for us died.
We shall un-der-stand, in the bet-ter land, Why the crown of thorns was worn.
Oh, do not de-lay, come to Him to-day, Soon will close the mer-cy gate.

CHORUS

On the cross,...... cru-el cross,...... Je-sus suf-fered for us
On the cross, cru-el cross, Je-sus suf-fered

all, Bleed-ing there,...... dy-ing there,...... He has
for us all, Bleed-ing there, dy-ing there,

saved us from the fall; On the cross,........ cru-el
He has saved us from the fall; On the cross,

On the Cross

cross,.... He His life did free - ly give,...... That we all ......
cru - el cross, He His life did free - ly give, That we all

who be - lieve,...... Might for - ev - er with Him live.........
who be - lieve, with Him live.

No. 55

Sweet Is Thy Love

James Rowe

J. R. Baxter, Jr., owner, 1917

J. R. Baxter, Jr.

1. Je-sus, my Friend for-ev-er, Sweet is Thy love to me, Nothing our hearts shall
2. Whether the storm be sweeping, Whether the sky be fair, I shall be in Thy
3. Sometime across the riv - er, Safe in that ho-ly place, Jesus, my Friend for -

sev - er, Ever Thine own I'll be. Feeling Thy love enfold me Close to Thy
keep-ing, Happiness will be there. Nearer, dear Master, nearer Draw me to
ev - er, I shall behold Thy face. Then, in the light of glo - ry, How I shall

precious side, Feeling Thine arms uphold me, Safe shall my soul a - bide.
Thy dear breast, Ev - er be-com - ing dear-er, All the way home to rest.
praise Thy love! How I shall tell the sto - ry With the redeemed a-bove!

No. 56   Better Than Gold

Copyright, 1937, by The Stamps-Baxter Music Co.

JAMES ROWE   VIRGIL O. STAMPS

1. Earth may give won-der-ful rich - es and fame, If to the temp-ter our
2. O in the strug-gle for rich - es be - low, Wor-ries op - press us and
3. Tho' all the world by our toil we might gain, Noth-ing at last we can

spir - its are sold; But if we work in the Blessed One's name, He will give
cares nev - er cease; But if we work for the Mas-ter, we know, We shall have
car - ry a - way; But the dear Savior gives what will remain, Blessing our

something far bet - ter than gold.
hap - pi - ness, com-fort and peace.
souls through an un - end - ing day.

Chorus

Bet - ter than gold, bet-ter than gold, Je - sus gives more than can
Bet - ter than gold,.............. bet - ter than gold,.............. Je-sus gives more,........... than can

than can ev - er be told; Give Him your days,
ev - er be told;.................. Give Him your days,..............

Better Than Gold

for when He pays, It will be something far bet-ter than gold.

for when He pays,

No. 57

Who Will Sing For Me?

Copyright, 1937, by The Stamps-Baxter Music Co.

J. T. E.

J. T. Ely

1. Oft I sing....... for my friends.... When death's.... cold form I see,
2. When the voice.... of my King...... Shall call....... me home a-bove,
3. But I know...... that at last....... With our....... life's rec-ord fair,
4. So I'll sing...... till the end....... And help - - ful try to be,

But when...... my life ends........ Will some one sing for me? (for me?)
O who...... then will sing.......... The part-ing song of love? (of love?)
With tri - - als all past.......... We all shall sing up there. (up there.)
As - sured ..... that some friend....... Will sing a song for me. (for me.)

CHORUS

I won - - der who.... Will sing .... for me?.... When I'm
    I won-der   will sing

called to cross the si - lent sea, Who will sing.......... for me?.......
        who will sing   for me?

No. 58   You'll Have to Lay it Down

Thomas Ramsey   Copyright, 1931, by V. O. Stamps   Virgil O. Stamps

Not too fast

1. In the quest for gold, thru the heat and cold, there are many souls to-day,
2. There are folks we know who in this life show they are slaves to fashion's ways,
3. There are ma-ny men liv-ing now in sin, bound by van-i-ty and pride,

Drift-ing farther from the e-ter-nal home and the good old gos-pel way;
We can see them fall as they give their all for a word of so-cial praise;
Trusting their own hand, thinking they will land in the home beyond death's tide;

They may here have pow'r thru the earthly hour, but they are not homeward bound.
But the fame they see will dis-card-ed be at the fi-nal trumpet sound.
But the on-ly way to the land of day, where the righteous wear a crown,

FINE

D. S.

You can-not take gold to heav-en,—you will have to lay it down.
It is out of style in heav-en,—they will have to lay it down.
Is by grace, thru faith in Je-sus, lay-ing ev-'ry-thing else down.

D. S.—*you will have to lay it down.*

CHORUS

You will have to lay it down, you will have to lay it down,
O, yes,

You'll Have to Lay it Down

If you want to en-ter heav-en and re-ceive a star-ry crown; You can

D. S.

nev-er take your gold into love's e-ter-nal fold,—If you want to get to heaven,

---

No. 59

Still it Stands

J. R. Baxter, Jr.
Chorus by James Rowe

Copyright, 1931, by V. O. Stamps

Virgil O. Stamps

1. Tho winds have fiercely blown From many sinful lands, It has not moved a sin gle
2. The skeptics rid - i - cule And join themselves in bands, God's power shall for-ev-er
3. The winds and waves obey The Savior's blest commands, He's coming back to earth some

rit.

CHORUS

stone, The church of God still stands. It stands, it stands Se - cure in His own
rule, The church of God still stands.
day, The church of God still stands. It stands, the church still stands

rit.

hands; Up-on the ev - er-last-ing rock The church of God still stands......
His church still stands.

No. 60   Paradise Valley

NOAH WHITE   VIRGIL O. STAMPS

1. As I trav-el thru life, with its trou-ble and strife, I've a glo-ri-ous
2. As I roam the hill-side, or I list to the tide, As I pluck the sweet
3. Tho your garden is rare, it is naught to com-pare With the flowers that

hope to give cheer on the way; Soon my toil will be o'er and I'll rest on that shore
flowers that grow in the dale; A faint picture is there of a land bright and fair
bloom in the garden a-bove, In the midst of it grows Sharon's perfect sweet Rose,

Where the night has been turned in-to day.
Where per-en-ni-al flow-ers ne'er fail.
'Tis the won-der-ful Flow-er we love.

CHORUS

Up in the beau-ti-ful par-a-dise val-ley, By the side of the riv-er of life,........
Up in par - - a - dise val-ley....... of the riv-er of life,

Up in the val-ley, the won-der-ful val-ley, We'll be free from all
Up in par - - a - dise val-ley, ...

Paradise Valley

pain and all strife; .... There we shall live in the rose-tinted garden,
from all pain and all strife; There we'll live in the gar-den, ...

'Neath the shade of the ev-er-green tree, ... How I long for the par-a-dise
of the ev-er-green tree, for the

val-ley, ... Where the beau-ty of heav-en I'll see........
par-a-dise val-ley, beau - - ty of heav-en I'll see.

No. 61   I Ain't Got Weary Feet Yet

SPIRITUAL

1. Been-a pray-ing for the sin-ner so long, And I ain't got wea-ry yet;
2. Been-a talk-ing to the mourners so long, And I ain't got wea-ry yet;
3. Been-a sit-ting up with sick folks so long, And I ain't got wea-ry yet;

D. C.—And I ain't got wea ry yet, And I ain't got wea-ry yet.

FINE D. C.

Been-a pray-ing for the sin-ner so long, And I ain't got wea-ry yet.
Been-a talk-ing to the mourners so long, And I ain't got wea-ry yet.
Been-a sit-ting up with sick folks so long, And I ain't got wea-ry yet.

Been-a do-ing what I can for so long, And I ain't got wea-ry yet.

No 62   At Sunset I'm Going Home

Rev. Johnson Oatman, Jr.   Copyright, 1927, by V. O. Stamps   Virgil O. Stamps

Not too fast

1. Just a lit-tle while to tar-ry in this vale of grief and tears,
2. How I love to watch the bright stars blaz-ing in the midnight sky,
3. When I see the sun at ev-'ning flam-ing up the ros-y west,

Just a few more wea-ry, wea-ry miles to roam;.............
How they gleam and glit-ter in yon span-gled dome;.............
Light-ing like a beam of gold the o-cean's foam;.............

Then I'm go-ing to that country where they count not time by years, For at
Then I think of that bright mansion I'll in-hab-it by and by, For at
I shall look up-on that mo-ment as the one su-preme-ly blest, For at

REFRAIN

sun-set I'm go-ing, go-ing home. Won-der-ful the sun-set, mar-ve-lous the
   Sun - set,   sun -

sun-set, my sun soon may set, How it gilds with gol-den glo-ry heaven's
set,   How   it   gilds heav'n's

At Sunset I'm Going Home

vault - ed dome; I am filled with singing, joy-bells now are ringing,
fair and vault-ed dome; Sun - set, sun - set,

I shall nev - er fret, For at sun-set I'm go-ing, go-ing home.

No. 63

Help Me to Find the Way

Thomas Ramsey, owner,

Thomas Ramsey

Good as Solo

1. Sorrow's dark clouds gather o'er me, My heart is burdened with care;
2. All of my life has been wasted, Noth-ing to of-fer have I;
3. I would a - bide with Thee ev - er, Guide me, O Mas-ter, I pray;

FINE CHORUS

Humbly I bow now before Thee, O Lord, please hear my pray'r.
Life's bitter cup I have tast ed, Sav-ior, don't pass me by. Troubles have
That I shall stray from Thee never, Help me to find the way.

D. S.—load, Lord, Help me to find the way.

D. S.

roughened my road, Lord, Anguish o'er-shadows my way; Let Thy love lighten my

O Could I Forget

R. F. Aingell, Jr.   V. O. Stamps, owner.   Virgil O. Stamps

1. O could I in love,............ for my Sav - ior for-
2. O could I for - get............. all the foes that con-
3. O could I for - get............. that in death cold and

get,............ The days that have filled............
trive............ My soul of its joy............
gray,............ This mor - tal shall still............

heart and soul with re - gret;........... Be - liev - ing that
and its peace to de - prive,........... And cling to the
in the tomb mould a - way;........... But know that the

D. S.—And trust in the

He........... ev - er with me will be,...........
Lamb,.......... since so tru - ly I've read...........
spir - - - it to glo - ry shall wing,...........

love........... of my Sav - ior di - vine,...........

My bur - dens to bear,........... my spir - it to
That pleas - ure for pain........... He giv - eth in-
For - ev - er to live........... with Je - sus my

Till heav - en - ly joys........... shall ev - er be

O Gould I Forget

FINE CHORUS

free.................... O could I for-get.................
stead.................
King............... O could I for-get

mine..............

the sor-rows I meet,.................. The foes that oft
the sor-rows I meet,

D. S.

try................... my soul to de-feat;.................
The foes that oft try my soul to de-feat;

NO. 65 ## Where He Leads Me I Will Follow *Arr.*

1. I can hear my Sav-ior call-ing, I can hear my Sav-ior call-ing,
2. I'll go with Him thru the gar-den, I'll go with Him thru the gar-den,
3. He will give me grace and glo-ry, He will give me grace and glo-ry,

D.C.-*Where He leads me I will follow, Where He leads me I will fol-low,*
ad lib. D. C. for Chorus

I can hear my Sav-ior call-ing: "Take thy cross and follow, fol-low me."
I'll go with Him thru the gar-den, I'll go with Him, with Him all the way.
He will give me grace and glo-ry, And go with me, with me all the way.

Where He leads me I will fol-low, I'll go with Him, with Him all the way.

No. 66   Get Your Shoulder Under the Cross

Rev. L. E. Green   Virgil O. Stamps

1. Get your shoulder un-der the cross, while you wait you're suf-fer-ing loss,
2. While you're standing i - dle to-day, time is swift-ly pass-ing a-way,
3. By and by when la-bor is done and the bat-tles all have been won,

For your soul can-not re-ceive the blessings it needs; (the blessings it needs;)
In the Master's har-vest field find something to do; (find something to do;)
And your soul is full of peace and won-der-ful love; (and won-der-ful love;)

Je - sus needs your ac-tive, true life in this world where e - vil is rife,
You may bring some beau-ti-ful sheaves, or re - turn with noth-ing but leaves,
When the Lord shall come for His own from His Fa-ther's beau-ti-ful throne,

If you're faith-ful you'll be blest for all of your deeds. (for all of your deeds.)
O the bless-ed Lord is now de-pend-ing on you. (de-pend-ing on you.)
With the saved and blest you'll go to man-sions a-bove. (to mansions a - bove.)

Chorus

Get your shoulder un-der the cross, get your shoulder un-der the cross,
Get your shoul - - - der un-der the cross, ...

Get Your Shoulder Under the Cross

God is need-ing work-ers in His vineyard to-day;
His vine-yard to-day;

Get your shoulder un-der the cross, get your shoul-der un-der the cross,
Get your shoul - - der un-der the cross,.............

Go and show the lost the true and beau-ti-ful way.
the beau-ti-ful way.

No. 67 **Jesus is Keeping my Soul**

Copyright, 1938, by The Stamps-Baxter Music Co.

H. R. Hale Reeves

BASS SOLO

1. Tho an-gry winds a-round me may blow, Bil-lows so mad-ly may roll;
2. I'm not a-fraid when Je-sus is near, There is no dan-ger for me;
3. When I shall come to cross o'er the tide, Near-ing the heav-en-ly goal;

I will be safe in Je-sus, I know, For He is keeping my soul.
All thru the day my pray'rs He will hear, What a great helper is He.
In that glad home I'll ev-er a-bide, Je-sus is keeping my soul.

No. 68   The Great Judgment Morning

Bass Solo with Quartet Chorus for men's voices. If used as Solo thruout D. S. for Chorus

Copyright, 1939, by Stamps-Baxter Music and Ptg. Co.

War Cry   in "Favorite Radio Songs No. 2"   **Virgil O. Stamps**

Recitativio

1. I dreamed that the great judgment morning Had dawned, and the trum-pet had
2. The rich man was there but his mon-ey Had melt-ed and van-ished a-
3. The wid-ow was there and the or-phan, God heard and remembered their
4. The mor-al man came to the judg-ment, His self-righteous rags would not

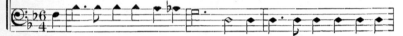

blown;   I dreamed that all na-tions had gath-ered, To judg-ment be-
way;   A pau-per he stood in the judg-ment, His debts were too
cries,   No sor-row in heav-en for-ev-er, God wiped all the
do,   The men that had cru-ci-fied Je-sus Had passed off as

fore the white throne; From the throne came a bright shining an-gel, And
heav-y to pay; The great man was there but his great-ness When
tears from their eyes; The gam-bler was there and the drunk-ard, And the
mor-al men too. The souls that had put off sal-va-tion, Not to-

D.S.—Then O what a weep-ing and wail-ing When the

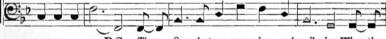

stood on the land and the sea, And swore with His hand raised to
death came was left far be-hind The an-gel that o-pened the
man who had sold them the drink, With the peo-ple who gave them the
night; I'll re-pent by and by; No time now to think of re-

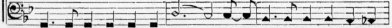

lost ones were told of their fate   They cried for the rocks and the

The Great Judgment Morning

D.S. Chorus

heav - en, That time was no long - er to be.
rec - ords, No trace of His greatness could find.
li - sence, To - geth - er in hell they did sink.
li - gion, But a - las they had found time to die.

Then O what a

Fine

moun-tains, They prayed but their prayers were too late.

weep-ing and wail - ing, When the lost were told of their fate; They cried for

the rocks and the moun-tains, They pray'd too late, too late.
but their prayers were too late. . . . .
ad lib.

No. 69 Thus Far The Lord

Dr. Lowell Mason

1. Thus far the Lord has led me on, Thus far His pow'r prolongs my days;
2. Much of my time has run to waste, And I, per-haps, am near my home;
3. I lay my bod - y down to sleep, Peace is the pil - low for my head;

And ev -'ry eve-ning shall make known Some fresh me-mo-rial of His grace.
But He for-gives my fol - lies past, He gives me strength for days to come.
While well ap-point-ed an - gels keep Their watch-ful sta-tions round my bed.

No. 70   I've Been List'ning in on Heaven

THOMAS RAMSEY   in "Harbor Bells No. 5"   VIRGIL O. STAMPS

1. I have had a hap-py vis-ion Of a dis-tant bet-ter land,
2. When my courage has been shak-en, And the blue skies turn to grey,
3. Tune your heart to heaven's wave-length, Thru the blest con-trol of pray'r,

There was not a sign of sor-row, Glad-ness ruled on ev-'ry hand;
E - vil forc-es oft - en tempt me, Try to turn me from the way;
Ground your faith in love e - ter - nal, Tune out sor - row pain and care;

Mu-sic flowed in sweet-est con-cords, 'Twas an end-less day of spring,
But there's something that will com-fort, Peace and glad-ness it will bring,
In the time of in - ter-fer-ence, Clos - er to the Sav-ior cling,

I've been list - 'ning in on heav-en, Just to hear the mil - lions sing.
When I'm list - 'ning in on heav-en, Just to hear the mil - lions sing.
While you're list - 'ning in on heav-en, You will hear the mil - lions sing.

CHORUS

I've been list-'ning in on heav-en, List-'ning to the songs of love,
List-'ning,..............   List-'ning,..............

I've Been List'ning in on Heaven

Sung by saints of all the a - ges, Prais-ing Christ in heav'n a - bove;

I've been list-'ning in on heav - en, And I heard their mu - sic ring,
List -'ning, ... List -'ning, ...

I've been list-'ning in on heav - en, Just to hear the mil - lions sing.

No. 71

Windham

DANIEL READ

1. Broad is the road that leads to death, And thousands walk to - geth-er there,
2. "De - ny thy-self, and take thy cross," Is the Re-deem-er's great command;
3. Lord, let not all my hopes be vain; Cre - ate my heart en - tire - ly new,

But wis-dom shows a nar-row path, With here and there a trav - el - er.
Na - ture must count her gold but dross, If she would gain this heavenly land.
Which hyp-o-crites could ne'er at-tain, Which false a-pos-tates nev-er knew.

My Dream of Mother

Mrs. R. L. Wall   Virgil O. Stamps

1. I dreamed I saw moth-er in heav-en, An an-gel so bright and so fair,.... As she sang in the bright courts of glo-ry, And walked in the man-sions up there;.. The face I had loved so in child-hood, 'Tis dear-er than life now to me,.. I pray to the Lord, I shall meet her, And there with her ev-er shall be.....

2. I dreamed I saw moth-er up yon-der, In gar-ments so pure and so white,.. As she wandered thru gates of the cit-y, Where nev-er comes shades of the night;.. It seemed to me that she was search-ing The heav-en-ly por-tals a-bove, Just look-ing and waiting my com-ing, With dear ones she once learned to love...

3. I dreamed I saw moth-er in heav-en, She sang man-y old songs to me,.... O the ones I once cherished so fond-ly, No songs ev-er sweet-er could be;.... She sang of the Sav-ior's sal-va-tion, And bade us to kneel at His feet,.. Ac-cept the great pardon He gives us, And life as my dream will be sweet..

CHORUS

I dreamed mother sang me to

My Dream of Mother

sleep, Gent-ly rocked and sang me to sleep, There is naught to com-
pare, with my glo-ry up there, If my moth-er can rock me to sleep...

rit. — *rit.*

rit. e dim.

No. 73 When I Reach My Home, Sweet Home

Rev. Johnson Oatman, Jr.   V. O. Stamps, owner, 1926   Virgil O. Stamps

1. I shall hear the harp of Da-vid ring, When I reach my home, sweet home;...
2. I shall talk with Adam there, I know,
3. I will talk with Peter, James and John,
4. But the best of all, my Lord I'll see,   reach   my home, sweet home,

FINE

I shall hear the Temple chorus sing, When I reach my home, sweet home....
Prophets, Priests and Kings of long a-go,
And with men and women long since gone,   reach   my home, sweet home.
I will praise Him thru e-ter-ni-ty,

D.S.—Saints of long ago I'll see and know, When I reach   my   home, sweet home.

CHORUS   D. S.

When I reach   my home, sweet home, When I reach my home, sweet home;...
When I reach my home, sweet home....   When I reach   my home, sweet home,

Keep Following On

Herbert Buffum   **Virgil O. Stamps**

1. When you from your sins have once turned away, And your load of guilt and
2. When answers to pray'rs seem no more to be, And deep in your heart you're
3. Some day you will hear the eve-ning bells toll, And heav-en up-on your

sin is all gone; What ev-er the test you meet by the way, Keep
mi-nus a song; Re-mem-ber that God the spar-rows can see, He's
vis-ion will dawn; Com-mit to your Lord the care of your soul, He'll

fol-low-ing on, (Keep fol-low-ing on,) Keep fol-low-ing
watch-ing you, too, (He's watch-ing you, too,) Keep fol-low-ing
car-ry you thru, (He'll car-ry you thru,) Keep fol-low-ing

Chorus

on. . . . . Keep fol-low-ing on, ... Keep
keep fol-low-ing on.   Keep fol-low-ing on,

ad. lib.

fol-low-ing on, ...
Keep following on, Tho dark be the night, just watch for the dawn;

Keep Following On

Till shadows have fled, ... Till darkness is gone, ...
Till shadows have fled, Till darkness is gone,

Keep fol-low-ing on, ... Keep fol-low-ing on ....
Keep fol-low-ing on, Keep fol-low-ing on.

No. 75 Mother

J. G. Warren, owner

Rev. L. M. Byers   J. G. Warren

1. Mother's gone be-yond death's riv - er, Just a - cross the storm - y sea;
2. O how sad to me the part - ing, How my heart was made to bleed,
3. I am sure my moth-er's wait-ing For her lone - ly or-phan child,

She is wait-ing for my com-ing, And she fond - ly looks for me.
When I said good-bye to moth-er, As her soul at death was freed.
Who of earth is grow-ing wea - ry And to death is rec - on - ciled.

Fine

D.S.—There no death can ev-er part us, 'Twill be one e - ter - nal day.

Chorus   **D.S.**

Yes, dear moth-er, I will meet you In that realm not for a - way;

The Stream Of Calvary

James Wells

Virgil O. Stamps

The Stream Of Calvary

rit.

to set me free,...... ...... My Lord was cru - ci - fied......
to set me free, My Lord

No. 77

Clinging To The Cross

J. S. Kimbrough

W. A. Stewart, owner.

W. A. Stewart

1. Tho' troub - les oft sweep o'er my soul, Temptation's bil-lows 'round me toss;
2. The pleas-ures of the world to me Are but as worthless, sor - did dross;
3. Life's rich-est joys that I have known, I free - ly count them all but loss;

I look be-yond, where lies the goal, And cling still clos - er to the cross.
I look be-yond them, Lord, to Thee, And cling yet clos - er to the cross.
Earth's glitt'ring prospects all dis-own, And cling un - to the bless-ed cross.

REFRAIN

The cross, the cross of Cal - va - ry, Oh! let it be my theme and song,

Till up - ward pressing, Lord to Thee, I join at last the blood-washed throng.

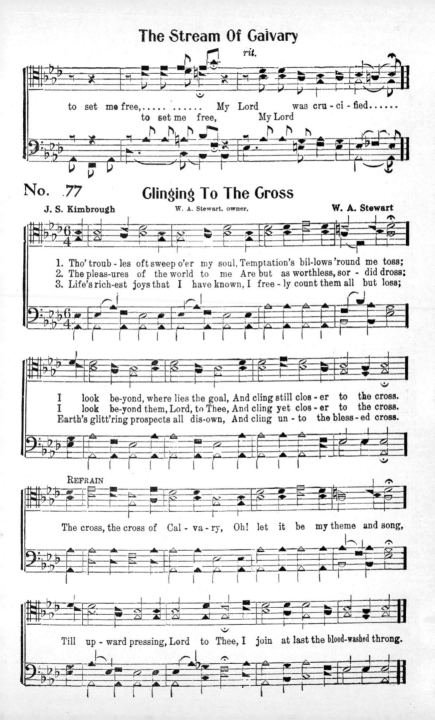

Dreaming Alone In The Twilight

V. O. S.

Virgil O. Stamps, owner

Virgil O. Stamps

1. Last night as dark-ness gath-ered, I sat dream-ing all a - lone,
2. The cot-tage on the hill-side And the spring be-neath the hill,
3. I dreamed of all the loved ones That have passed be-yond the tide,

I dreamed of childhood's play-mates, And the hills we used to roam;
The laugh-ter of the chil - dren, And the rip-pling of the rill;
I dreamed I saw the cit - y, And the gates swung o - pen wide;

I saw their hap-py fac - es, And their voi-ces came to me
Came to me in my dream-ing, Just as plain as yes - ter - day,
The Sav - ior bade me wel-come, And I glad - ly en - tered in,

As full of joy and sun-shine, As in days that used to be.
And I was for the mo-ment There a - gain a child at play.
For - ev - er free from sor - row And for - ev - er safe from sin.

CHORUS

I was dream - ing,.... dream-ing a - lone, I was
dream-in, in the twi - light,

Dreaming Alone In The Twilight

dream - ing of my dear old happy home; Childhood's scenes once more
dreaming of my child-hood's
3d v. dream - ing of my friends and loved ones gone, When with earth I'm thru,
dream-ing of my dear old

came and knocked on mem'ries door, I was dreaming a-lone in the twi - light.
then my dreams will all come true, I was dreaming a-lone in the twi - light.

No. 79   Bloom Brightly, Sweet Roses

C. L. SHAW   Used by permission   E. B. FOWLER

Slowly, with feeling

1. Bloom brightly, sweet ros-es, bloom brightly a - bove The mound that en-
2. O tell to the weep - er, in whis-per-ings low, 'Tis well with the
3. Then blossom, sweet ros-es, your fragrance be-stow On him who re-

clos - es the form that we love; Dif - fuse o'er His bo - som
sleep - er, who's rest-ing be - low; O tell us the spir - it
pos - es in si - lence be - low; Thy lan - guage, un - spok-en,

Rit.

the sweetest per-fume, From each glowing blos-som that smiles o'er His tomb.
of Him that we love Has gone to in - her - it the king-dom a - bove.
is more to my heart Than an - y love-to - ken that friends could im - part.

No. 80 The Best Things of Life are Free

Copyright, 1937, by The Stamps-Baxter Music Co.,
in "Harbor Bells No. 6"

Arr. V. O. S.—L. G. P. VIRGIL O. STAMPS

1. How oft-en you long for the treasures you see, Wish-ing you could claim
2. Kind words of a friend when your out-look is blue, How they brighten your
3. Trust not in the rich-es of sil-ver and gold, Just re-mem-ber God

them for your own; For-get-ting the best things of this life are free,
hope, like the dawn; The beau-ty of flow-ers that bloom just for you,
sits on His throne; It costs you no mon-ey to en-ter His fold,

Sweetest treasures that the world has ev-er known.

CHORUS

You can't
You can't buy the sunshine

buy the sun-shine at midnight, You can't buy the moonlight at dawn,
at mid-night, . . . You can't buy the moonlight at dawn, ...

You can't buy your youth, when you have grown old, Nor life when your
Nor your life when your heart-beat is

The Best Things of Life are Free

heart-beat is gone; You can't buy the love of a moth-er,
gone;......... You can't buy the love of a moth-er, ...

Nor child - hood a - gain at her knee, Al- tho you may
Nor child-hood a - gain at her knee, ...

hold earth's sil -ver and gold, The best things of life are free..........
best things of this life are free.

No. 81
On Zion's Hill

Copyright, 1937, by The Stamps-Baxter Music Co., in "Harbor Bells No. 6"

M. M. McK.   M. H. McKEE

1. On Zion's hill a mansion stands For all the pure and blest, We know it was
2. No sun or moon is shining there To light the streets of gold, The Lamb's own
3. To meet you there I mean to live While here on earth I stay, There Christ a

D. S.—The soul's e - ter-nal home; God's voice is

FINE CHORUS   D. S.

was not made with hands, Up there the soul may rest. On Zi - on's blessed hill,
light so wondrous fair The saints with joy behold.
wel-come sweet will give For one e- ter- nal day.   On Zi-on's

soft- ly call-ing still To rest beneath that dome.

No. 82 — Memories

James Wells in "Favorite Radio Songs No. 2" Virgil O. Stamps

1. When the eve-ning shad-ows lengthen, When the sun sinks in the west,
Oft-en times I fall to think-ing Of the loved ones gone to rest,
O-ver in the land e-ter-nal, In that ci-ty by the sea, Loved ones
gone from earth for-ev-er, Watching o-ver there for me. (for me.)

2. Gold-en mem-'ries, half for-got-ten, Of the friends of long a-go,
'Mid the mag-ic of the eve-ning, Come to me in cease-less flow,
Days of care-less, hap-py childhood, When a lad at moth-er's knee, In the
gloam-ing, in the wildwood, Roaming hap-py, care-less, free. (so free.)

3. Moth-er dear in heav-en wait-ing For your boy to wan-der home,
Long my wea-ry, wand'ring footsteps In the earth-ly path must roam,
Guide my wayward, er-rant footsteps, Where-so-e'er my path may be, That when
life on earth is o-ver, I may come back home to thee. (to thee.)

Chorus

Mem'ries, mem-'ries, mem'ries of long a-go, Mem'ries of loved ones,

Memories

wait-ing there I know, Lord, so guide me, guide my wan-d'ring

feet, So that some day, my loved ones a-gain I'll meet. I'll meet.
ad lib.

No. 83   ## Pass Me Not

"Whosoever shall call upon the name of the Lord shall be saved."

Fanny J. Crosby   W. H. Doane

1. Pass me not, O gen - tle Sav - ior, Hear my hum - ble cry;
2. Let me at a throne of mer - cy Find a sweet re - lief;
3. Trust-ing on - ly in Thy mer - it, Would I seek Thy face;
4. Thou the Spring of all my com-fort, More than life to me,

Fine

While on oth - ers Thou art smil - ing, Do not pass me by.
Kneel-ing there in deep con - tri - tion, Help my un - be - lief.
Heal my wound-ed, brok - en spir - it, Save me by Thy grace.
Whom have I on earth be - side Thee, Whom in heav'n but Thee?

D.S.—While on oth - ers Thou art call - ing, Do not pass me by.

Chorus   **D.S.**

Sav - ior, Sav - ior, hear my hum - ble cry,

No. 84   A Light in the Window of Heaven

Thomas Ramsey   **Virgil O. Stamps**

Slow

1. How well I re-mem-ber when I was a boy, I wandered from home oft at night; But when I re-turned it would give me great joy To see an old lamp burn-ing bright.

2. I knew that a wel-come was wait-ing for me, My moth-er was al-ways so kind; Tho search where you may, moth-er al-ways will be The best friend a boy e'er can find.

3. Our cot-tage was dark when I came home one night, The Sav-ior had called moth-er home; To join heav-en's cho-rus, in gar-ments of white, Where sor-row and death nev-er come.

Rit.

Chorus

There's a light in the win-dow of heav-en tonight, My mother is praying, (is) pray-ing for me, She is ask-ing her God to watch o-ver her boy, To

A Light in the Window of Heaven

keep him where e'er he may be; That light will still guide me where

ev - er I roam, I know it will keep, keep the way clear, It will
the way clear,

lead me some day to that beau-ti-ful home, To be with my mother dear.
moth-er dear.

No. 85   **Our Loving Mother**

Wm. Wade Beshears   Nina Todd

1. We have lost our loving mother, Home is dark and empty now; And our hearts are
2. She was ev - er true to Je-sus, To her loved ones, home and friends; Now her just re-
3. Let us all prepare to meet her, Turn away from paths of night; Let us heed her

D.S.—To that home where angels dwell; May we meet her

Fine Chorus   **D.S.**

filled with sorrow, But to Je-sus we will bow.
ward she's reaping With her Lord where bliss ne'er ends. Mother dear has gone to heaven,
lov - ing precepts, Trust in Christ and live aright.

in that ci - ty Nev-er more to say fare-well.

Talk It Over With Jesus

Thomas Ramsey   Virgil O. Stamps

1. O broth-er strug-gling on-ward 'neath a bur-den of de-spair,
2. If   you are per-se-cut-ed by some mem-bers of your church,
3. When you are grow-ing fee-ble from the man-y years of pain,

Your bod-y grow-ing weak-er with your trou-ble and your care;
When friends have turned a-gainst you and your good name would be-smirch;
When age has wrecked your bod-y and your health you can't re-gain;

When your en-e-mies ap-proach you, do not fal-ter in the fight,
If   it seems your soul is sink-ing and your way is dark as night,
If   it seems the way is dark-er from the dim-ness of your sight,

Chorus

Talk it o-ver with Je-sus, He will make it right. Talk it o-ver with

Je-sus and com-fort will be found,   Tell Him all of your trou-bles,
                joy   there   will be found,

Talk It Over With Jesus

weth-er day or night; Get your knees acquainted with the cold and rock-y
cold and

ground, Talk it o - ver with Je - sus, He will make it right.
rock-y ground,

No. 87   Sitting At the Feet of Jesus

Rev. K. C. Minter   Minter and Davis, owners   J. W. Davis

1. Sit - ting at the feet of Je - sus, Watching, waiting ev -'ry day; Trust-ing
2. List'ning at the feet of Je - sus, His com-mand to go or stay; Trust-ing
3. Seek-ing still the feet of Je - sus, I would seek no oth- er place; For 'tis
4. When the toils of life are o - ver, When my race on earth is run; May the

Fine   Chorus

in His grace and pow-er, Safe to keep me all the way.
al - ways in His wisdom, Safe to guide when I o - bey. Sit-ting at the feet of
there I claim the prom-ise Of the full-ness of His grace.
eve'ning shadows gath'ring Find me there when day is done.

D.S.—Drive the shadows from my way.

Je - sus, Where I love to kneel and pray, Till His good-ness and His glo - ry,

Coming

J. R. Baxter, Jr.   V. O. Stamps, owner.   Virgil O. Stamps

1. Je - sus is com-ing from heav - en Back to the earth some day,
2. Some day the clouds will be lad - en With a most pre - cious King,
3. E - ven the an - gels in heav - en Know not the day nor hour,

Will you be found where faithful are crowned, Or be turned a - way from His
He will de-scend, our glo - ri - ous friend, While na - ture shall sing of His
But thru the maze on one of these days We'll see Him in pow'r brot from

jew - els? O He will come back in His glo - ry O - ver the earth to
glo - ry and In - to sub-jec-tion all na - tions Low at His feet shall
heav - en, for He will be giv - en do - min - ion O - ver the land and

reign, Hast-en, my brother, get read - y, Gath-er in the grain.
lie, He will be crowned with true glo - ry, Lord and King most high.
sea, O what a glo - ri - ous rul - er Will our Sav - ior be.

CHORUS

He is com - ing Back to the earth a - gain,
Coming, coming, coming, coming,

Coming

Coming in love from heaven a-bove, To reign o-ver men; He is
Coming, coming, coming, coming, To reign o-ver men;

Com - ing to reign o - ver men;

coming in pow - er, glo - ry, O what a sight 'twill be!
Coming, coming, coming, coming,

Saints on the earth will greet Him with mirth, The King is He......
Coming, coming, coming, coming, Coming, coming, King is He.

Saints will greet Him, King is He......

No. 89 Nearer, My God, to Thee

Sarah F. Adams

Lowell Mason

1. Near-er, my God, to Thee; Near-er to Thee; E'en tho it be a cross
2. Tho' like a wan-der-er, The sun gone down, Darkness be o-ver me,
3. There let the way ap-pear Steps un-to heav'n; All that Thou sendest me,

D. S.—Near-er, my God, to Thee,

D. S.

FINE

That rais-eth me: Still all my song shall be, Near-er, my God, to Thee,
My rest a stone; Yet in my dreams I'd be Near-er, my God, to Thee,
In mer-cy giv'n; An-gels to beck-on me Near-er, my God, to Thee,

Near - er to Thee!

No. 90   Beyond the Clouds

in "Super Specials"

V. O. S.   Virgil O. Stamps

1. Beyond the clouds of greed and ha-tred, Beyond the gloom of war and
2. Beyond the clouds of dis-ap-point-ment, Beyond the heartache, pain and
3. Beyond the clouds at death's dark riv-er, Beyond the part-ing here be-

sin, Be-yond the low-'ring clouds of sor-row The sun will
care, Be-yond the drear-y days of toil-ing The sun is
low, Be-yond the hours of trib-u-la-tion The sun will

soon shine thru a-gain; Do not de-spair when days are dark-est,
al-ways shin-ing there; Thru faith look past the clouds a-bove you,
shine a-gain we know; The Lord is on His throne in heav-en,

Do not lose hope when clouds hang low, Be-yond the clouds the sun is
Reach up and grasp the Sav-ior's hand, Be-yond the clouds the sun is
He e-ven notes the sparrow's fall, Be-yond the clouds the sun is

Chorus

shin-ing, 'Twill soon break thru with cheer-ful glow.
shin-ing, 'Twill soon break thru to bless the land.
shin-ing, 'Twill soon break thru to bless us all. Be-yond the

Beyond the Clouds

No. 91   Going to Heaven

Rev. O. S. Jones   in "Pearly Gates"   Virgil O. Stamps

1. In the path of beau-ty I am trav-'ling now, Since the bless-ed Sav-ior touched my heart with love; Joy is ev-er pres-ent for the way is bright, I will fol-low Je-sus to my home a-bove.

2. Once I lived in sad-ness and my heart was lone, But my Sav-ior found and took me in His care; He the shad-ows lift-ed, shed His light a-round, Now I glad-ly fol-low Je-sus an-y-where.

3. No more days of sor-row shall af-fect my soul, No more doubt and sad-ness bow my spir-it low; I am trust-ing Je-sus and will not turn back, I am hap-py as t'ward Beu-lah-land I go.

Chorus

O what a hap-py day when Je-sus washed a-way All my All my guilt-y stains, my guilt-y stains, O praise Him, Gone all my sad dis-tress, and on-ly

Going to Heaven

hap - pi - ness, Now re - mains;
re - mains, now on - ly hap - pi - ness re - mains; I'm

Joy - ful - ly bless- ing Him, glad - ly con - fess-ing Him, Lord and
my Lord and

King, I am con - fess - ing glad - ly, O hal - le - lu - jah, I'm

go - ing to heav - en, And sing, sing, sing.
for - ev - er, ev - er sing.

Coda

I'm go - ing home, I'm go - ing home, I'm go - ing home to die no more.

No. 92 Sweeping Through To Glory

Hebert Buffum   Virgil O. Stamps

1. Sweep-ing thru to glo - ry with the glo - ry in my soul, Shout-ing hal - le-
2. Sweep-ing thru to glo - ry tho I have the glo - ry now, Then I came to
3. Sweep-ing forth thru tri-als that can nev - er hin - der me, For just like a

lu - jah! while the days so swift-ly roll; On the hal - le - lu - jah line where
Je - sus and be - fore Him I did bow; He for-gave this sin - ner, washed me
bird on wing I'm hap-py, glad and free; Soon I'll join the num - ber that John

ev'ry soul is glad, Sweep-ing thru to glo - ry, O how can we then be sad?
in His pre-cious blood, Shed up-on the tree where it poured forth in crim-son flood.
saw in gar-ments white, Where for-ev-er-more I'll dwell be-side the throne of light.

Chorus

I am sweep - - - ing thru to glo - - ry With the
Sweep-ing thru to glo - ry with the glo - ry in my soul,

glo - - - ry in my soul,
Sweep-ing thru to glo - ry with the glo - ry in my soul,

Sweeping Through To Glory

Once I was a sin - ner, But the Sav-
Once I was a sin-ner but the Sav-ior made me whole, Once I was a sin-

ior made me whole; Ver - y soon I'll
ner but the Sav-ior made me whole; Soon I'll hear the an - gels

hear the an - - gels Sing as I ap-proach the
sing as I ap-proach the goal, Soon I'll hear the an-gels sing as

goal, Then I'll be in glo-
I ap-proach the goal, Then I'll be in glo - ry, then I'll be in

ry For I've glo - - ry in my soul.
glo - ry, glo - ry in my soul, down in my hap-py ran-somed soul.

No. 93   Sweetest Story Ever Told

James Rowe   Virgil O. Stamps

1. O the sweet-est sto - ry that was ev - er told to men Is the sto - ry of the Savior's love, (the Savior's love,) We have heard it o'er and o'er and love it more and more, For it tells us of a home a - bove; If we hear it when we're sad, it quick-ly makes us glad, And it lights us thru the shadows dim, Noth-ing bet - ter can be heard, it is His e - ter - nal word,

2. There are man-y still who wait to hear the sto - ry told, For their hearts are are ver-y sad in-deed, (are sad indeed,) They are in the downward way and sin - ning ev - 'ry day, So its light and cheer and peace they need; Let us pray for cour-age true, our du - ty here to do, That His mes-sage we to them may give, Let us bid them look a - bove, with as - sur - ance of His love,

3. By and by when life is o'er and bur - dens all laid down, Then the sto - ry we may tell on high, (may tell on high,) In His pres-ence we shall rest, no more to be opprest, With our friends and all the an - gels nigh; So re- peat the bless-ed news, that man the Lord may choose, And receive the pow - er of His grace, For who-ev - er will be-lieve on the Sav - ior shall re-ceive

Sweetest Story Ever Told

Chorus

And it leads the lost to Him.   'Tis the best   that is told
Let us bid them look and live.
Entrance to that happy place. 'Tis the sweet - est sto-ry told,   The blessed

Of   His   love, His   precious love,   It is played,
sto - ry of the Sav-ior and His love,   And it is played   on harps of

harps of gold By   angel throngs above;   Let us tell   it o'er and
gold   a-bove; Let us tell   it o'er and

o'er and o'er   To   the lost while   days go by,
o'er   To those astray while days and years are going by,   That

Sing it there,   more and more, When we reach our home on high.
we may sing   it ev-er-more,

That Day is Coming Soon

J. R. Baxter, Jr.   Virgil O. Stamps

1. There will come a bless-ed time, When the bells of heav'n will chime,
2. O   the time is draw-ing near, Let   us face   it with-out fear.
3. Let   us on-ward march a - long, Giv - ing out   a cheer-ful song

Trou-bles then will quick-ly fly, While the Lord comes from on high;
We are on-ly   go-ing home Where no more   our feet will roam;
To the wea-ry   on the road, Help-ing bear   the heav - y load;

All   the saints will then re - joice When they hear His   wel-come voice,
What a hap-py tho't to   be From our fet - ters   all set   free,
We shall have a wel-come there When the saints meet   in the   air.

No more tears,   thru the years,   And that
sor-row, pain nor tears,   glad e - ter - nal years,

CHORUS

day   is com-ing soon..... When the clouds..... back-ward roll.......
                            When the clouds   back-ward roll,

That Day is Coming Soon

Sun will shine, light di - vine, Let us
Then the sun will bright-ly shine, we shall see the light di-vine,

press..... t'ward the goal,... Work-ing morning, night and noon; **Fix your**
Let us press t'ward the goal,

eyes...... on the crown,... Paid we'll be
Fix your eyes on the crown, We shall all re-ward -ed be when the

Lord we see, Heav'n for us......... will come down,....
bless - ed Lord we see, Heav'n for us will come down,

And that day is com - ing soon...... ....
we know sure - ly com - ing soon.

Skies Will be Blue

al - ways true, And the world will take.......... on a bright-er
right al - ways true,   world will take

hue;   Tho the storms in fu - ry may blow when Je-sus
and the skies will be blue,

speaks "Peace be still," The tempests cease,.... and o - bey His will:.........
                          Tempests cease   at His will;

Tho the night may hide .... heaven's shining view,.....
     Night may hide   heaven's view, When shall dawn the

the   skies   will   be blue.....................
day, storms will all pass away and the skies be blue. (and the skies will be blue.)

Praise the King

Thos. F. Johnson   V. O. Stamps, owner, 1925   Virgil O. Stamps

1. March stead-i - ly on, prais-ing the Lord in hap - py cho - rus,
2. Toil, pa-tient-ly toil, true to the Mas - ter and to du - ty,
3. On, prais-ing the King, let-ting your best to Him be giv - en,

Keep-ing bright, spread the light, wor - ship and a - dore;
Watch and pray, nev - er stray, nev - er yield to sin;
Look a - bove, trust His love, while on earth you roam;

God's beau - ti - ful light ev - er is shin-ing bright-ly o'er us,
Your loy - al - ty show, grow-ing in grace and fade-less beau - ty,
On, joy - ous - ly on, till with a song you en - ter heav - en,

Close a - bide, to His side, trust-ing more and more.   On, on, on,
March a - long, and be strong, vic - to - ry to win.   On, ...
There to rest, with the blest, in that home, sweet home.   On, ...

CHORUS

     on, on, on,   Keep the stand - ard
cheer-ful - ly on, ... Keep-ing the stand-ard lift - ed

Praise the King

high, keeping it high;   On, on, on,   on, on, on,
high; .... Stead-i-ly on,........ joy-ous-ly on,........

We'll be-hold Him soon there in the sky;
We shall be-hold Him by   and   by;............... Ev-er go

On,   on,   on,   on,   on, on,   Soon we'll
on,........ stead-i-ly on,........ Soon He will greet us

see His smile, beau-ti-ful smile;   Yes, we will all be at
with   a   smile;.......... We will be............. safe at

home, hap-py and free, In a lit- tle   while.............
home,............   ver-y lit-tle while, aft-er a-while.

No. 97 On With a Song

James Rowe V. O. Stamps, owner, 1925 Virgil O. Stamps

1. Work-ers are need-ed by the heav-en-ly King, Up and a-way,
2. Car-ing no lon-ger for the pleas-ures that stain, Up and a-way,
3. Soon will the har-vest time for-ev-er be past, Up and a-way,

serve Him to-day; Sheaves for His glo-ry let us will-ing-ly bring,
serve Him to-day; Help-ing the Bless-ed One to gath-er the grain,
serve Him to-day; We shall be-hold His face in glo-ry at last,

CHORUS

Up and a-way, O loy-al reap-ers. On with a
On with a song, with a

song, ... Joy-ous and strong, ...
hap-py song,
hap-py song, so joy-ous and strong, ev-er sweet and strong, And

Fol-low the Mas-ter in-to the field;
fol-low the Har-vest Mas-ter in-to the har-vest field;

On With a Song

Faith-ful re-main, the life-crown to gain, Help-ing Him to

gath-er in the pre-cious yield; O on with a
On with a song, with a

song,..... fear-ing no wrong,........
ring-ing song, earth-ly wrong,
ring-ing song, and fear-ing no foe and no earth-ly wrong. For

soon will the reap-ing time be gone; Shadows will soon be fall-ing,

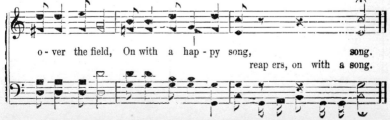

o-ver the field, On with a hap-py song, song.
reap-ers, on with a song.

No. 98   Joy in Going On

J. R. Baxter, Jr. Suggested by V. O. S.   Virgil O. Stamps

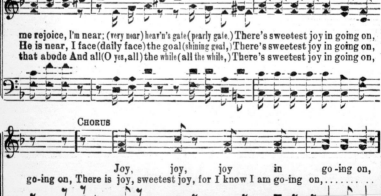

1. Not a cloud (to-day) as I tread (life's way,) My Lord is the light, the sun-shine bright,
2. Storms may come (my way) yet I have (a stay) In Him who can lead, with manna feed,
3. Come with me (dear friend) where the joys (ne'er end,) Then you shall be glad and never sad,

He leads (ev-er leads) me straight (O so straight) Until the drear-y night is gone,
And keep (ev-er keep) my soul (trusting soul) Un-til the cur-tain has been drawn,
He'll make (He will make) you smile (quickly smile) And you shall see the fadeless dawn,

it is gone; I can talk (with Him) when the path (seems dim) And His gentle voice makes
backward drawn; With my friend (and guide) ev-er by (my side) I shall nev-er fear for
fadeless dawn; Turn a-way (from sin,) a new life (begin,) There's no other road to

me rejoice, I'm near; (very near) heav'n's gate (pearly gate.) There's sweetest joy in going on,
He is near, I face (daily face) the goal (shining goal,) There's sweetest joy in going on,
that abode And all (O yes, all) the while (all the while,) There's sweetest joy in going on,

CHORUS

Joy,   joy,   joy   in   go-ing on,
go-ing on, There is joy, sweetest joy, for I know I am go-ing on,........

Joy in Going On

Joy, joy, joy to see the dawn,
There is joy, sweetest joy, for I know I shall see the dawn,...... I'll see that

Home for which I always yearn I shall ne'er return, for there I shall
home for which I yearn And from it I shall ne'er re - turn

have per-fect joy; Joy, joy, joy in precious love,
There is joy, sweetest joy, just to think of His precious love.....

Joy, joy, joy, march home a-bove, Teach it,
There is joy, sweetest joy, in the march to the home above,.. O pilgrim teach it,

sing it, preach it, ring it, Joy, joy, joy, joy in go-ing, go-ing on.
sing it, preach it, ring it, sweet-est, great-est on......

No Shadows Fall

fair, All is joy, peace and love In that
bright and fair, All is joy, peace and love In that

home a - bove; Beau - ti - ful home where all the
home, beau- ti- ful home a - bove;

saved and blest Shall find per - - fect
All the saved and the blest There shall find

rest, In that home of the soul while a - ges shall
per - fect rest,

roll No shad - - ows fall..............
No dark, wea - ri - some shades ev - er shall fall, shad - ows fall.

No. 100 I've Been Redeemed

V. O. S.

Copyright, 1926 by Virgil O. Stamps

Virgil O. Stamps

1. My life is filled with gladness, I've been redeemed, I've been redeemed,
2. My soul is filled with sing-ing,
3. I'm on my way to glo - ry, I've been re-deemed,

No tho't have I of sad-ness, I've been re - deemed;
The joy-bells now are ring-ing,
I'm sing-ing love's old sto-ry, I've been redeemed, yes, I've been redeemed;

In dark ness once I wan-dered, No light up - on me beamed, But
The road that I am trav-'ling, Is bright er than I dreamed, And
I've cast a - way sin's bur - den, It was not what it seemed, And

now my heart is sing-ing, I've been redeemed, redeemed.
it is growing brighter,
now I'm shout-ing hap-py, yes, I have been redeemed.

I've been redeemed.

I've Been Redeemed

REFRAIN

I've been redeemed, I've been redeemed. My soul is
I've been re-deemed, My soul

free, my soul is glad and free, The Savior came, He glad-ly came.
is free; The Sav - - - ior came

and ransomed me, He came and ransomed me, The wond'rous joy,
and ran - - somed me, The joy

the joy that fills, The joy that fills, that fills my soul to - day
that fills my soul to - day

accel.

Is caus-ing me to shout and sing a - long the pil-grim way.
the pil-grim way.

No. 101   I Am Going

J. R. Baxter, Jr.   Copyright, 1927, by V. O. Stamps   Virgil O. Stamps

1. I am go-ing up to heav-en fair When my pil-grim-age on
2. I am go-ing up to glo-ry-land There to wear a robe so
3. I am go-ing to an end-less home, Don't you want to go a-

earth is o'er, And I know I'll meet my loved ones there, When I
pure and white, And I want to hold my Sav-ior's hand, In that
long with me? There no more my feet shall ev-er roam, Thru the

reach that hap-py gold-en shore; But best (but best) of all (of all) the
cit-y where there is no night; No winds (no winds) to blow (to blow) and
a-ges of e-ter-ni-ty; And you (and you) may have (may have) His

Lamb who died for me, His love to show, will wel-come me, I know,
fill my soul with fear, So glad and free, how hap-py I shall be,
love your soul to thrill, He calls for you, His prom-is-es are true,

Chorus

When His smil-ing face I see.   I am
Liv-ing with my Sav-ior dear.
One is "who-so-ev-er will."   I am go-ing o-ver

! Am Going

go - ing o - ver there, To a land su - preme - ly fair,
there............. To a land su - preme - ly fair,...............

Land that's fair - er far than this,
'Tis a land of bliss that's fair - er far than this, Where my

where I'll rest;.... When I reach that home on high,.............
soul shall find sweet rest; When I reach that home on high,

I shall nev - er weep or sigh,................ But to Christ, my King, for-
I shall nev - er weep or sigh, But to

ev - er I shall sing, In that home-land of the blest.............
Christ I'll ev - er sing, In that bright homeland of the blest.

home of the blest..........

Ye Reapers of the Lord

V. O. Stamps, owner, 1926

Virgil O. Stamps

1. Speed a - way, ye reap-ers, haste to the har-vest field, Ripe and white the
2. Rain may soon be fall-ing, shad-ows a-round you lie, For the hours of
3. When all work is end-ed, when all the grain is stored, Great shall be your

har-vest, gather the precious yield; Arms of love shall keep you, ev - er shall
la - bor speed-i - ly pass and die; Speed a-way, ye reap-ers, keep-ing the
glo - ry, great the di-vine re-ward; So be brave and loy - al, trust-ing the

be your shield, Saving grace shall keep you true; (surely keep you true;)
Spir - it nigh; And your ut-most glad-ly do; (and your utmost do;)
might-y Lord, Who has giv - en all for you; (giv-en all for you;) O reapers,

Heed the call of Je - sus, an-swer and speed a - way, While the light is
Harm shall not be-fall you, Je-sus your souls will keep, Wheth-er foes be
With a song of glad-ness gath - er the gold-en grain, He will bless each

shin-ing, while it is called to - day; Cour-age shall be giv - en, Je - sus will
near you, whether the storms shall sweep; Work for Him with gladness, sheaves for His
ef - fort, ye shall not toil in vain; In His bless-ed serv-ice, loy - al to

Ye Reapers of the Lord

CHORUS

be your stay, Till the la-bor time is thru...
glo - ry reap, Till the la-bor time is thru...
God re-main, Till the la-bor time is thru...

reapers of the Lord, true
love shall safely shield, yes,

Ye reap - ers of the
His love your souls shall

reapers of Christ, the Lord, Cheer-ful-ly la-bor on, yes, cheerfully la-bor on,
surely His love shall shield, Till all the day has gone, the wearisome day has gone,

Lord, work on, be true,
shield, till day has gone,

1

win-ning the re-ward, all win-ning the great re-ward, wait-ing a-
And win the great re - ward that waits

2

bove for you, now wait-ing a-bove for you; In the har-vest field, yes,
for you; So in the har - vest

out in the harvest field, Trusting the Holy One, work on.
field, work on, work on. (for the Lord work on.)

No. 103 HE WILL BE WITH ME.

James Rowe.

Virgil O. Stamps.

1. Who-so-ev-er may be be-fore me In the wea-ri-some
2. Ma-ny tri-als I shall be bear-ing, Ere I come to the
3. Soon will end all my earth-ly sto-ry, Soon my tri-als will

gos-pel way; Whether black-ness or blue be o'er me, While
pear-ly gate, But the Sav-iour for me is car-ing, Till
all be past, Then a-bove I shall share His glo-ry, And

work-ing for Him each day; I shall still be in His dear keep-
mine are the joys that wait; I am sure He will nev-er leave
look on His face at last. So I rest in His bless-ed keep-

ing, In His love will my spir-it be; So I'll still car-ry
me, And from sin He will keep me free; So I fear not what
ing, And I trust where I can-not see, And shall trust till I

on the reap-ing, For my Sav-iour will be with me.
things may grieve me, For my Sav-iour will be with me.
end the reap-ing, For my Sav-iour will be with me.

HE WILL BE WITH ME. Concluded.

CHORUS. *Alto prominent.*

He will be with my soul ev - 'ry hour of the
He will be near, near to my soul each min - ute and hour and

day,.......... He will keep me His own ev - 'ry
all of the day, Oh, He will keep, keep me His own each

step of the way;.......... 'Till at heav - - en's bright
step of the way, each step of the way; 'Till at the gate,

gate His dear face I shall see,............. I
heav-en's bright gate the face of my Lord and King I shall see,

know my Re-deem - - er will be with me.
Sure- ly I know Je - sus, my Friend, will ev-er be walk-ing with me.

No. 104　Reapers Haste Away

V. O. S.

Virgil O. Stamps, owner

Virgil O. Stamps

1. O see the gold-en har-vest Wait-ing on ev-'ry hand; Bend-ing in
2. Now is the time for reap-ing, Why sit ye i-dly by? Sum-mer will
3. Soon will the grain be wast-ing, Go while the fields are white, Soon will the

eve-ning breez-es, O-ver the en-tire land; Je-sus, the har-vest mas-ter,
soon be o-ver, Win-ter is draw-ing nigh, This is no time for pin-ing,
night be fall-ing, Go while then yet 'tis light; Je-sus, the Mas-ter needs you,

Points to the field a-way, So grasp ye the wait-ing sic-kle,
Work while it yet is day, So grasp ye the wait-ing sic-kle,
Wag-es to you He'll pay, So grasp ye the wait-ing sic-kle,

Chorus

Haste　a-way.　Go to the har-vest field, O

Haste to the field a-way, O reap-ers. Go.............. in-to the

go to the har-vest field, Go gath-er the precious yield, the

field.............. And gath-er in.............. the pre-cious

REAPERS, HASTE AWAY.

No. 105 Jesus Taught Me How to Smile

J. R. Baxter, Jr. Copyright, 1930, by V. O. Stamps Virgil O. Stamps

1. Once I was sad, nev - er felt glad, The path was dark to me,
2. All the day long I had no song, My nights were sleepless, too,
3. Why bear your load on life's rough road When blessings wait for you?

Clouds hid the skies, so my tired eyes No ray of hope could see;
I found no joy in sin's em-ploy Be-cause my life was blue;
Cling to His hand, He'll un-der-stand For He's a friend so true;

But one sweet day on life's rough way, I found a friend worth while,
When Je-sus came, O praise His name, He smoothed my roughest mile,
Give Him your heart, bid sin de-part, Let grace your soul be - guile,

He made me whole, saved my poor soul, He taught me how to wear a smile.
He gave me cheer, ban-ished my fear, He taught me how to wear a smile.
Thru each glad day your soul will say: He taught me how to wear a smile.

CHORUS

Je - sus taught me to wear a smile When the
Je - sus taught me how to wear a smile When the path is

Taught me to smile On

Jesus Taught Me How to Smile

path is dark and drear - y, Made me see things
dark and drear,.......... Made me see the

paths drear, Made me see the things so

that are worth while, Drove 'way doubt and fear;
things that are worth while, Drove a - way my doubt and fear;

worth while, Drove 'way doubt and fear, and

Fol - low Him all a - long life's way,
Now I can fol - low where He leads a - long life's way,

Now I can tread life's path - - way,

Strength He gives for ev-'ry rough mile, When to Him I
Strength He gives for ev - 'ry mile, ...

Strength He gives for each mile,

pray, then I can tru-ly say: "Jesus taught me how to smile.".........
"Je - sus taught me to wear a sun-ny smile."

Christ

No. 106   Drink of the Fountain of Life

James Wells   V. O. Stamps, owner, 1919   Virgil O. Stamps

1. Would you wear....... a crown e-ter-nal   In the land....... be-
2. In that ci - - ty bright, transcendent,   There your friends .... and
3. Why, O why........ still long-er wan-der   In the ston - - y

yond the skies,   In that ci - - ty bright, su-per-nal,   In the
loved ones wait,   In their robes...... of white resplendent,   Close be-
paths of sin?   It is time........ to stop and pon-der,   If to

realms ...... of par - a - dise?   Then drink from...... the liv-ing
side.......... the gold- en gate.   Would you win...... the heav'nly
heav - - en you would win;   See the fount...... so free- ly

foun-tain,   Which im - mor - - tal life will give,   Fount that
guer-don?   Would your friends .... and loved ones see?   Cast, O
flow - ing,   Pre - cious foun - - tain of Christ's blood,   Par-don

flows.... from Calv'ry's mountain,   O drink from.... the fount and live.......
cast...... a -way sin's bur-den,   Drink ye from.... that fount so free.......
full ...... on all be- stow-ing,   Drink, O drink ... of it's pure flood ......

Drink of the Fountain of Life

No. 107 — My Dream-Home in Glory

Rev. W. A. WASHBURN   VIRGIL O. STAMPS

1. There's a won-der-ful dream-home in glo-ry, "In a land where we'll nev-er grow old," That we've heard of in song and in sto-ry, 'Tis a ci-ty whose streets are pure gold; Here on earth I'm a lone, wea-ry pil-grim, And I know I don't have long to stay, But I'll set-tle in glo-ry for-ev-er, In my dream-home just o-ver the way.

2. In that dream-home of mine o-ver yon-der, Not a thing that I need is de-nied, Oft-en times in my dreams do I pon-der, Pear-ly gates that now stand o-pen wide; There the ros-es are bloom-ing e-ter-nal, And no dark dis-ap-point-ments will come, All my prayers of the past will be answered, When I'm safe in my hap-py dream-home.

3. O that dream-home of mine o-ver yon-der, It is more than just mere-ly a dream, It is not just a sad dis-al-lu-sion, Like our fond-est hopes here some-time seem; For my Sav-ior has gone to make read-y, Man-y man-sions for all who will come, He has made me a ti-tle in glo-ry To my hap-py e-ter-nal dream-home.

My Dream-Home in Glory

Chorus

Won-der-ful dream-home, dream-home in glo-ry, Where all of my
O my dream - - home in glo-ry, Where all

dreams will come true, Beautiful dream-home, dream-home in glory,
of my dreams will come true, O my dream home in glo-ry,

Some day I would share it with you; We can live in that dream-land for-
Some day I would share it with you;

ev - er, In that home where we'll nev-er be blue, Why
In that home where we'll nev-er be blue,

don't you arrange it with Je - sus And make it your dream-home, too?
And make it your dream-home, too?

No. 108

Onward We Go

Jas. Wells

V. O. Stamps, owner, 1919

Virgil O. Stamps

Spirited

1. On-ward we go as we fol-low our King, Shout-ing the
2. On-ward we go as our Lord leads be-fore, Fight-ing all
3. On-ward we go with our Lord and our King, Fol-low-ing

vic-t'ry cry; Still press-ing on-ward, His prais-es we sing,
wrong and sin; With our Lord's ban-ner de-fi-ant-ly o'er,
all the way; Know-ing that vic-to-ry He'll sure-ly bring,

Cer-tain that vic-to-ry's nigh; Fight-ing for right ev-er
Vow-ing the fight we will win; See Sa-tan's forc-es
Noth-ing our course can de-lay; On-ward we press for our

loy-al and true, Wag-ing war a-gainst sin; Keep-ing our
in full re-treat, As we press on our way; Forc-es of
God and the right, Sure we will nev-er fail; Safe and se-

Mas-ter's cause e'er in view, On-ward we press till we win.
e-vil must meet de-feat, On-ward we press ev-'ry day.
cure we in Je-sus' might, Know-ing that He will pre-vail.

Onward We Go

Chorus

On - ward,
On-ward, on - ward, on-ward we go, Vic-to-ry

On- ward, on-ward, ev- er, on- ward, on-ward soon the

He will bring; On-ward, on - ward, on-ward we go,

On- ward,

On-ward, on-ward ev- er,

Fol-lowing Christ our King, Fight-ing for Christ, yes, for God and right;

Sure- ly we'll win, we shall win the fight, Trust-ing in God all the

way is bright, On, stead-y on, on till we win.

till we win.

No. 109 SWEET HARBOR BELLS

Virgil O. Stamps

1. When the bil - lows rise and roll, Comes this com - fort to my soul,
2. O the hope that they im - part To the wea - ry storm-tossed heart,
3. Till the bless - ed morn shall dawn, Bless - ed bells ring on and on,

Sweet har-bor bells, ring on,............... Precious mes-sage
sweet har-bor bells; Tell - ing us that
Ring on,.............. ring on,............... Till our Pi - lot's

from the strand Of the bless-ed glo - ry-land; Ring on, ring
home is near, Bid-ding us be of good cheer;
face we see, Ev - er more our comfort be; sweet har-bor bells,

CHORUS f

on............... Oh, hear them ring, Giving com-fort ev - er
sweet har-bor bells. Ring on,...............

cres.

more; What cheer they bring from the hap - py gold - en shore.
Ring on,...............

SWEET HARBOR BELLS

No. 110   Sing of His Love

V. O. S.   V. O. Stamps, owner   Virgil O. Stamps

1. Sing of the love of the Sav - ior, Sing of the love of the King,
2. Sing of the love of the Fa - ther, Who sent His Son un - to men,
3. Sing all ye peo - ple who love Him, Sing of the debt that He paid,

An - thems of love and thanks-giv - ing, Un - to the Sav - ior bring,
For He sent Heaven's bright jew - el, Woo-ing them back a - gain,
Give to Him hon - or and glo - ry, In Him your hope is stayed,

Sing of His won-der-ful good - ness, Sing of His mar-vel-ous grace,
Sing of His plan of sal - va - tion, Un - to a world lost in sin,
Sing of the Heav-en that's wait - ing, All the re -deem-ed on high,

Praise Him in an-them and sto - ry, Till you be-hold His face. (His face.)
Tell all the world of His good - ness, Help them a crown to win. (to win.)
Sing of the glo - ri - ous meet - ing, In the "sweet bye and bye." (and bye.)

Sing of His Love

Chorus

Wonderful love,
Sing of His wonderful love, Sing of His marvelous

Marvelous grace, Wonderful, glorious,
grace, Wonderful love, glorious love,

Rit.

Wonderful love,
Love that redeems the race, Sing of the price that He

Price that He paid, Cross that He bore,
paid, Sing of the cross that He bore, He came to

Rit.

Wonderful, marvelous, Sing, sing, sing evermore.
die, for you and me, Sing evermore.

No. 111 I Would Not Miss It—Would You?

Herbert Buffum in "Joyful Songs" Virgil O. Stamps

1. If Christ should return in the clouds before night, I would not miss it, would you? And ris-ing to greet Him His saints took their flight; O I would not miss it, would you? When those in the tomb once a-gain live a-new, And once more a-rise and ap-pear on our view, When for-ev-er and ev-er with earth we are thru, O I would not miss it, would you?

2. We've prayed for a might-y re-vi-val to come, I would not miss it, would you? It will come when with-in our own hearts 'tis be-gun; O I would not miss it, would you? When God shall come forth in the same old-time pow'r, And on those who look old-time bless-ings will show'r, Sup-pos-ing it does come this ver-y same hour! O I would not miss it, would you?

3. When sin-ners cry out as they cried long a-go, I would not miss it, would you? And Chris-tians the full-ness of God's love would know; O I would not miss it, would you? When wrongs are made right and forgiveness is sought, And free-ly be-stowed as of old we are taught; When no man but love owes his fellowman ought, O I would not miss it, would you?

I Would Not Miss It—Would You?

Chorus

The bless - ed Re-deem - er Is soon to ap-pear,
Bless-ed Re-deem - er, bless-ed Re-deem - er, Soon to ap-pear,

The time of "the com - ing
is soon to ap-pear, Time of His com-ing, time of His com - ing,

A - gain" draw - eth near; With shouting and sing-ing till
The time of His com - ing draw-eth near;

all heav-en rings, We'll crown Him for-ev - er the King of all kings, With

mem'ries that saddened for-e'er taken wings, O I would not miss it, would you?

No. 112 When the Day of Judgment Dawns

V. O. S.

Virgil O. Stamps, owner, 1921

Virgil O. Stamps

Not fast

1. When the judgment day at last shall dawn, And the an-gel of the Lord shall
2. When the trumpet of the Lord shall sound, And the dead shall rise from land and
3. O I pray you that you stop and think, For you soon may stumble o'er the

1. He
stand, With one foot up-on the rag-ing sea, And the
sea, Some will rise to gain the heav'n-ly prize, Oth - ers
brink, Make your call-ing and e - lec - tion sure, And your
there shall stand,

oth - er one up-on the land; (on the land;) When in ring-ing tones He
then will live in mis - er - y. (mis-er-y.) Will you be a - mong the
hope in Je - sus Christ se-cure, (yes, se-cure,) Take the Lord as pi - lot

then pro-claims That all time up-on the earth is o'er, Will you stand a-
ones who sing Hap - py prais-es to the Lord and King, Or will you in-
friend and guide, Keep Him ev - er close-ly by your side, Then when life up-

mong the saved and blest, (and blest,) When at last you reach the oth - er shore.
to the dark-ness go, (darkness go,) There to dwell in mis - er - y and woe.
on the earth is done, (is done,) You will hear the Mas-ter say "Well done."

When the Day of Judgment Dawns

Chorus.

When the day of judgment dawns o'er all the land and
When the day of

all the sea, Dead shall rise to heav-en's prize or
sea, And the

hell and mis-er-y, Will you shout the praise of
mis-er-y, Will you shout the

Christ with all the hap-py blood-washed throng? Or will you
blood-washed throng? Or will you be

rit.

be turned a-way When the day of judg-ment dawns.
turned a-way

Joy for Me

J. R. Baxter, Jr.　　　　　　　　　　　　　　　　Virgil O. Stamps

1. Joy is wait-ing me yon-der, sweet the tho't that I pon-der,
2. Soon my spir-it is go-ing where no tem-pests are blow-ing
3. La-bor soon will be end-ed, love-light then will be blend-ed,

Tho' on earth I now wan-der, I'll reach home; Loved ones ready to
And my soul will be know-ing things of worth, Sor-row nev-er can
And the lad-der as-cend-ed to the goal; Joy-bells sweetly be

meet me, naught can ev-er de-feat me, Christ is wait-ing to greet me
reach me, Je-sus ev-er will teach me, He won't have to be-seech me
sound-ing liv-ing wa-ters a-bound-ing, Pleasures they are im-pound-ing

CHORUS

'neath that dome. Joy............... will be mine some day,............
as on earth.
for my soul. I'll have glory some day, yes, joy and glory some day

Cares............... all will pass a-way,...............
For all my sorrows and cares will soon be pass-ing a-way, And

Joy for Me

I shall ev-er be singing, tributes unto Christ bringing, Hear the golden harps,

ring - ing, that will be joy for me; Home............... where I'll
Home where I shall soon rest,

sweet-ly rest,............... Live............... with the
sweet home where I shall soon rest, And there for-ev - er I'll live,

saved and blest,..................... Tell the sto - ry,
with all the saved and the blest, I'll

share His glo-ry, 'Twill be joy for me............. ......
'Twill be joy for me, per-fect joy for me.

No. 114   The King of Glory Hail

Laurene Highfield   Virgil O. Stamps, owner, 1923   Virgil O. Stamps

1. The King of glo-ry hail,   With heart and mind and voice, His glo-ry
2. The trees all clap their hands,   The hills lift up their heads, A-dor-ing
3. The King of glo-ry hail,   the breath of life He gave, From the grim

bursts up-on the sight, And makes the soul rejoice;   So great His maj-es-
Him who o-ver all His gold-en sun-light sheds;   He made the deep blue
tyr-an-ny of death His peo-ple He will save;   So wise His pre-cepts

ty,   So end-less is His might, That all the earth and sky and sea
sea,   He formed the fer-tile plain, From out His boun-ty free-ly gives
are,   So ten-der is His care, Let all who dwell up-on the earth,

Chorus

Praise Him with keen de-light.   Hail now the glo-ri-ous King,
Re-fresh-ing dew and rain.   Hail!   hail!   hail!
Hail Him, His worth de-clare.   Hail,   hail   the King,

All hail,   all

He is the mon-arch supreme,   Hail Him whose countenance sheds a
Hail!   hail!   hail!   Hail!   hail!   hail, a
Hail!   hail   the King,   Hail,   hail   the King,

hail,   All hail,

The King of Glory Hail

light whose glo-ries gleam,
Crown Him with glo-ry and praise,
Crown with praise,
Crown, crown the King,

Hail, hail, all hail, all

Hail the great giv-er of life, Praise Him who has full do-min-ion,
Hail! hail! hail! Hail! hail! hail! He
Hail, hail the King, Hail, hail the King, He

hail, All hail,

rit. *a tempo*

rules all fear and strife, Hail now the glo-ri-ous King, Laud Him who
Hail! hail! hail! Hail!
Hail, hail, the King, Hail,

Hail, hail, all hail, all hail,

reigns on His throne, Wisdom and glory and might, Are His and His a-lone.
hail! hail! Hail! hail! hail! The King who reigns alone.
hail the King, Hail, hail the King,

All hail, The King who reigns a-lone.

No. 115 There Will be no Disappointments

Mrs. Rilla Evans   Virgil O. Stamps

DUET *Slow*

1. We will meet with dis - ap - point-ments As we jour - ney far and
2. We should meet our dis - ap - point-ments With a brave and cheer - ful
3. There will be no dis - ap - point-ments And no tears where Je - sus

near, Of - ten we will be dis - cour-aged By some gos - sip
smile, Nev - er doubt the love of Je - sus, Skies will bright-en
is, There is peace and joy e - ter - nal In that home for

that we bear; When a friend or dear com-pan - ion Fails to
af - ter while; For the time is sure - ly com - ing When He'll
all of His; We shall have no great temp-ta - tions, All our

stand the slight-est test, Then the heart is filled with sor-row And the
roll the clouds a - way And our hearts will be re - joic-ing On the
tri - als will be o'er, Joy be-yond our ex - pec - ta - tions On that

CHORUS *Faster*

mind is sore op - pressed. Be no dis-appointments, dis-ap-
dawn-ing of that day.
fair and sin - less shore. There will be no dis - ap - pointments

There Will be no Disappointments

pointments,   Home a - cross the deep and mys - tic sea,
In that home a - cross the   sea,............ Je - sus

Made it all so per-fect, all so perfect,   Yes, for you and
made it all so   per-fect,   Beau-ti - ful for you and

beau - ti - ful for me;   Sin and e - vil can-not grieve us,   Friends and
me;............

DUET *Slow*

loved ones will not leave us,   Be no dis - ap-
There will be no dis - ap-

a tempo

pointments, disappointments,   All e - ter - ni - ty, e - ter-ni - ty.
pointments,   Thru-out all e - ter - ni - ty............

No. 116 Follow the One All-Glorious

James Rowe
V. O. Stamps, owner, 1919
Virgil O. Stamps

1. March a-long, ... fol-low the King, (Christ, the King,) Follow Him in the
2. Sing His praise, ... glorious praise, (endless praise,) Joyously praise His
3. Fol-low Him .... all the way home, (safely home,) Keeping Him always

up - ward way; Vic- to-ry sure (vic-t'ry sure) Jesus will bring, (He will bring,)
pow'r to save; Harmonies grand (always grand) heartily raise, (sweetly raise,)
ver - y near Do - ing His will, (do His will,) trav-el along, (march along,)

Fol-low Him closely day by day; He is the might-y One, all glo - ri-ous;
Knowing that He His life-blood gave; He is the ho - ly and su - per - nal One;
Fill-ing the world with gospel cheer; Soon we shall leave the gloomy sto-ry land;

accel.

He is the King of kings vic- to - ri -ous, And with His ban - ner o - ver
He is the Sav - ior, the e - ter-nal One Whose praise shall rise from sun to
Soon with the King be safe in glo - ry-land, With an - gels sing - ing on the

Chorus *a tempo*

us, un-spot-ted we shall stay.
sun, whose flag shall ev- er wave. Soldiers, on, on, on with the mighty One, We are
stand, with friends to us so dear.

Follow the One All-Glorious

We are safe with Him, we know, The need-ed grace He
safe with Him, we know; The need-ed grace He will be-

will be-stow, To tri-umph o - ver ev -'ry foe; The
stow, To tri-umph o - ver ev -'ry foe; The Lord of

Lord of earth and sky is He; Fol-low Him wher-
earth and sky is He; To fol-low Him wher-e'er He

e'er He leads, And find de-light in no-ble deeds, For He sup-
leads, And find de-light in no-ble deeds,

accel.

pli - eth all our needs, And leads us on to vic-to - ry.
He sup-pli - eth all our needs,

TELL HIM NOW
(FOR HE CANNOT READ HIS TOMBSTONE WHEN HE'S DEAD.)

Anon. Arr. by V. O. S.

Virgil O. Stamps

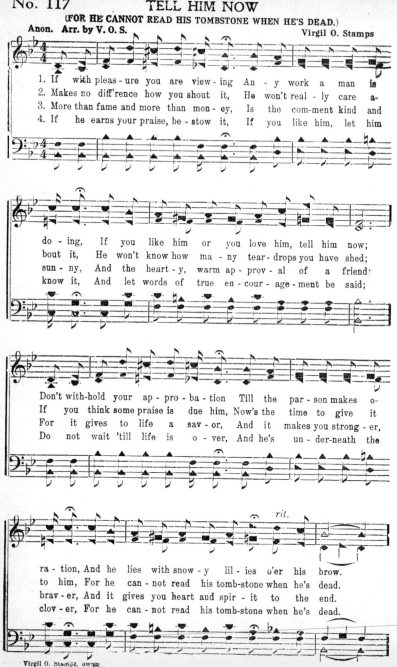

1. If with pleas-ure you are view-ing An-y work a man is
2. Makes no diff'rence how you shout it, He won't real-ly care a-
3. More than fame and more than mon-ey, Is the com-ment kind and
4. If he earns your praise, be-stow it, If you like him, let him

do-ing, If you like him or you love him, tell him now;
bout it, He won't know how ma-ny tear-drops you have shed;
sun-ny, And the heart-y, warm ap-prov-al of a friend:
know it, And let words of true en-cour-age-ment be said;

Don't with-hold your ap-pro-ba-tion Till the par-son makes o-
If you think some praise is due him, Now's the time to give it
For it gives to life a sav-or, And it makes you strong-er,
Do not wait 'till life is o-ver, And he's un-der-neath the

rit.

ra-tion, And he lies with snow-y lil-ies o'er his brow.
to him, For he can-not read his tomb-stone when he's dead.
brav-er, And it gives you heart and spir-it to the end.
clov-er, For he can-not read his tomb-stone when he's dead.

TELL HIM NOW

Chorus

Tell him now,........ Don't neg-lect to tell him, tell him now,
right now, to tell him now, ...

Place your hand in ap-pro-ba-tion on his head,............ Tell him
on his head,

now;........ Don't for-get to tell him, tell him now,
right now; to tell him now,.................

For he can-not read his tomb-stone when he's dead................
when he's dead.

Coda

When he's dead, when he's dead, No, he can-not read his tomb-stone when he's dead.
when he's dead.

No. 118 Oh! Praise The Lord

V. O. S. Virgil O. Stamps, owner, 1924 Virgil O. Stamps

1. We meet to-day............ to swell the praise............Of
2. Un-grate-ful we........would sure-ly be............If
3. We know that we,............a-cross the sea............In

God's own Son who once was slain, On the cru-el tree............
we re-fused His praise to sing, For He loved us more............
heav'n shall nev-er cease to sing, We will shout His praise............

........free-ly gave His life,............But now in heav'n He
........than His own dear life,............O let us make the
........thru the end-less days,............With an-gels we shall

lives a-gain; Then let us all....................with voic-es
glad songs ring; Some day a-bove....................where all is
praise our King; So let us then....................be read-y

glad,............Join in the songs that we shall sing, In praise to
love,............The saved shall sing a sweet-er song, An-ti-ci-
when............The Lord shall call for us to go, And while we

Oh! Praise The Lord

Sleeper, Awake, Arise!

N. W. Allphin   Virgil O. Stamps, owner, 1925   Virgil O. Stamps

1. O sleep-er, a-wake, make no de - lay, Too long you have slept, be-
2. O sleep-er, a-wake, a - rise and shine, And Je - sus shall give you
3. O sleep-er, a-wake, gird on your sword, Glad ser-vice to do for

hold, 'tis day, The sun in his strength is shin - ing now, A-
light di - vine; The voice of the Lord comes ring - ing clear, Do
Christ the Lord, And un - der His ban - ner for - ward go, Here

cross the sum - mer skies; The day-beams in beau - ty
not His call de - spise; Then up and a - way, your
striv - ing for the prize; The time of your tri - umph

shine so bright, Then tar - ry you not till falls the night, No
du - ty do, For vic - t'ry here may de - pend on you, Sit
may be near, Let zeal for His cause dis - pel all fear, The

long - er de - lay, O sleep - er, we pray, A - wake, a - rise.
not i - dly by, nor slum - ber - ing lie,
fight has be - gun, the war must be won, A-wake, a- wake, a - rise.

Sleeper, Awake, Arise!

CHORUS

Sleep-er, a-wake! sleep-er, a-rise,

A - wake,........ a - rise,........ Hear, O
Sleep-er, a-wake, sleep-er, a-rise,

O hear the clar-ion

hear you the call, Go forth to ser-vice while 'tis day, For

call,.........

night shades soon will fall; The King of the day now bids you rise,

He shines in His strength from sum-mer skies, No time must we lose,

So do not re-fuse, A-wake, a - rise.... ......
A-wake, a-wake, a-rise, O a-rise.

No. 120 — A Call to Praise

Laurene Highfield
Virgil O. Stamps, owner, 1920
Virgil O. Stamps

1. All ye ransomed chil-dren of the heav'nly King, Come seek His courts and loud hal - le - lu - jah's sing, Re-joice in Him who set you free from grief and death and pain; Sing for joy that He has seen your need of Him, And filled life's cup of bless-ing un - to the brim, Re-joice in Him, the ho - ly One, who ev - er - more shall reign.

2. All ye fa-vored people who have known His love, Stand forth and serve Him loy - al and faith- ful prove, Pro-claim to all His way is right and fills the heart with joy; Be ye glad that He has set His king-dom here, That to His throne His peo-ple may yet draw near, He brought to them the death-less life that noth - ing can de -stroy.

3. All ye chos- en peo-ple whom the Lord has called, Be glad in Him and be not by sin ap-palled, For He will give you strength to fight and win the vic - to - ry; Go ye on re - joic- ing as life's hill you climb, Cling to the Sav - ior ev - er in faith sub-lime, Be glad in Him as you press on -ward, till His face you see.

A Call to Praise

Chorus

Sing ye who have claimed the prom-ise, Laud
Sing, joy-ous-ly sing, Laud Je-sus the Lord,

Je-sus in strains of glad-ness, Sing an-thems of joy-ous
Sing, joy-ous-ly sing,

prais-es, As life's way you take; (sing hal-le-lu-jah;) Praise
Praise, joy-ful-ly praise,

Him who has brought salvation, Praise, bow-ing in ad-o-ra-tion,
Praise, joy-ful-ly praise,

En - ter in His courts with song, Sing praises till the ech-oes wake.
O en-ter His courts,

No. 121   It Will Not be Long

J. R. Baxter, Jr.   Sug. by V. O. S.   Virgil O. Stamps

1. Time is swift-ly fly - ing, chang-es come each day,   Hear a
2. We should not grow wea - ry tho the way is rough,
3. Let's be up and do - ing, Je - sus bids us shine, Soon we'll hear a

glad new song, hear a glad new song;   Rest and joy is com - ing,
                    At the jour-ney's end - ing
glad new song;..................... We've no time to lose till

let us work and pray,   And I know that it will not be long.
we'll find joy e - nough,
safe a-cross the line, And it won't be ver - y long................

Chorus

It will not be long   till we   be - hold, An - gels
           be long un - til we shall be - hold,

stand-ing by the great white throne up yon - der, O the joy to
               throne up yon - der,

It Will Not Be Long

live   and ne'er grow old, Sing-ing with loved ones all the while our
      to live and ne'er grow old,

hearts   grow   fond - er;   It   will not   be   long   **to**
hearts grow   fond - er;   It   will not   be   long   to

tar - ry   here   In   the   val - ley where our feet   are   prone   to
tar - ry   here   In   the   val - ley where our feet   are prone   to

wan - der,   Let   us   do   our   best   and
wan - der,   Let   us   do   our   best   and

have   no   fear,   For   it   will not,   O   it   will not be long.
have   no   fear,   For   it   will not   be   long......................

Right Will Always Win

James Rowe Virgil O. Stamps, owner **Virgil O. Stamps**

1. On - ward, O ye men of Zi - on, Zi - on, Fol - low Jud-ah's mighty
2. Cheer and hope to oth - ers giv - ing, giv - ing, For your lead-er's glo-ry
3. At the por-tals He will meet you, meet you, With a smile of sun-shine

Li - on, Li - on Of His pow - er tell - ing, keep - ing prais-es swell -ing,
liv - ing, liv - ing; To the lost ap - peal-ing, mer - cy sweet re -veal-ing,
greet you, greet you; Let - ting noth-ing sev - er, shout-ing "Christ for-ev-er."

Down with sin,
He will al -ways be a-
Down with sin, yes, down with doubt and sin (for) Homes for you He is pre-

hold (up-hold) you. Grace and pow - er shall in - fold, in - fold you, On-ward,
bove (a-bove) you, He will al - ways lead and love you, love you, En- e-
par- (pre-par-) ing, Where His throne you shall be shar-ing, shar-ing; On-ward,

up - ward ev - er, Joy shall crown en-deav-or, Right will win.
mies be -tide you, But with Him to guide you,
then, re - joic-ing, end- less prais - es voic-ing, Right will al-ways win.

Right Will Always Win

Chorus

Right will win, yes, the right will
On - ward, O ye le-gions of the mighty Lord, Onward for His glo - ry,

win, Right will win, For love keeps you
On-ward to reward, For storms in vain shall sweep you, Love divine will keep you,

free from sin: Right will
You shall triumph o-ver sin; your soul's shall surely triumph, Tell and sing the story

win, yes, the right will win, ev - er In His
Bring the wayward in; Give to God the glory, Warn them of their sin, and

cause delighting, Car -ry on the fighting, Right will always win.
is sure to win.

No. 123 THE MAN BEHIND THE PLOW

Dedicated to my class of 85 pupils, Beckville, Texas, Aug., 1915

Arr. by V. O. S. and C. F. Simons

VIRGIL O. STAMPS

1. There's been a lot to say a-bout the man be-hind the gun, And
2. A bat-tle-ship's a won-der, and an ar-my mighty grand, There's
3. In all the pomp and splendor of an ar-my on pa-rade, And
4. We're building mighty cit-ies and we're gain-ing loft-y heights, We're

folks have praised him highly for the no-ble work he's done; He
something sort of thrill-ing in the flag that's wav-ing high, We
thro' the aw-ful dark-ness that the smoke of bat-tle made, In
win-ning lots of glo-ry and we're set-tings things to rights, We're

won a lot of hon-or for the land where men are free, It was he that
all a-dore this grand old flag, the em-blem of our land, And it makes you
halls where jew-els glit-ter and where shouting men debate, In the pal-ace
show-ing all creation how the world's affairs should run, Future men will

sent our en-e-mies all back a-cross the sea, But, he's had his day of
want to hol-ler when the boys go marching by, But when all the shoutin's
es where rulers deal out hon-ors to the great, There is not a sin-gle
gaze in wonder at the things that we have done, But they'll ov-er-look the

glo-ry and his lit-tle spree, and now There's an-oth-er to be
ov-er and the fighting's done, some how We will find we're still de-
per-son who'd be do-ing busi-ness now, Or have med-als if it
fel-low, just the same as we do now, Who's the whole concern's foun-

The Man Behind the Plow

Mother And Dad

To my own Mother and Dad

Since this song was written in 1923, Dad has "crossed the river" to his reward,
Mother is still with me, waiting for the "great reunion" after a while—V. O. S.

V. O. S.   Virgil O. Stamps

1. In a home far a-way there's a cou-ple to-day, And their hair is as
2. In my mind oft I roam to the old coun-try home And my moth-er and
3. I am sure that I've strayed from the path that they made, For they walked with the
4. Soon they'll cross o'er the foam to their heav-en-ly home That has long been pre-

white as un-tram-pled snow; Their old fa-ces once fair are seamed now with care,
dad in fan-cy I see 'Round the al-tar at night, by dim can-dle light,
Lord each step of the way; But their pray'rs won for me a par-don so free,
pared and wait-ing for them, O how hap-py they'll be when Je-sus they see,

Chorus

They're the best friends I've had, my moth-er and dad.
They would pray for this lad, my moth-er and dad. My moth-er and
Thank God that I had such a moth-er and dad.
Nev-er more to be sad, my moth-er and dad.

dad,................ the best friends I've had, Will
My moth-er and dad, the best friends I've had,...............

soon cross the wa-ters cold   To dwell in a land,............... a
                                   To dwell in a land,

Mother And Dad

rit. e dim.

beau-ti-ful land,.......... ..... Where no-bod-y ev-er grows old.
a beau-ti-ful land,

No. 125 Deep In His Love

Mrs. Frank M. Lynn   Frank M. Lynn

1. Deep in His love se-cure-ly I rest, Free and con-tent, I'm hap-py and blest,
2. Deep in His love there's nothing to fear, He will de-fend, will comfort and cheer,
3. Deep in His love, O let me a-bide, Sheltered am I, so close to His side,

Lost to the world, its sor-row and woe, Trusting His guidance, on-ward I go.
Storms harm me not for peaceful am I In His sweet care while a-ges go by.
Till I shall reach that heav-en-ly home, Nev-er a-gain from Je-sus to roam.

CHORUS

Dai-ly my soul joy-ous-ly sings, Deep in His love and un-der His wings:

Sheltered from harm, so sweetly I rest, Deep in His love, I'm won-drous-ly blest.

No. 126 Sweeter the Story Grows

Geo. W. Winningham V. O. Stamps, owner, 1919 V. O. Stamps

Alto prominent

1. Often I've heard how the Lord from the sky, Came in His glo-ry for sin-ners to
2. Often I've read how He stood by the sea, Healing the stricken in sweet Gal-i-
3. O - ver and o - ver the sto-ry's been told, Hope of my soul, it will nev- er grow

die; And as the years with their burdens roll by, Sweet-er the sto-ry grows.
lee, Since He has promised a man-sion for me, Sweet-er the sto-ry grows.
old: Till we in glo - ry the Sav-ior be-hold, Sweet-er the sto-ry grows.

Chorus

Sweet - er it grows Bless-ed sto - ry so
Sweet-er it grows, sweet-er it grows, Sto - ry so sweet, blessed

sweet, Sweet-er and sweet-er it grows; Af -
sto - ry so sweet, yes, it grows; Af -ter the years,

ter the years And the joys and the tears,
af - ter the years, Af- ter the years and the joys and the tears,

Sweeter the Story Grows

Sweet-er and sweeter the sto-ry grows, Sweeter and sweet-er it grows.
still sweeter it grows.

No. 127   We Need Each Other

James Rowe

Virgil O. Stamps, owner, 1920

Virgil O. Stamps

Slow. Good as Solo

1. I'm keep-ing close to my Sav-ior, dear, And for His glo-ry I la-bor here;
2. I'm help-ing oth-ers His light to see, And He gives comfort and cheer to me;
3. I tell the sto-ry where-e'er I go, And He de-fends me from ev'ry foe;

We walk to-geth-er a-long the way, And need each oth-er from day to day.
And so we trav-el along the road That leads to heaven—our true a-bode.
And so, tho' tempted from Him to roam, He keeps me faithful and leads me home.

Chorus

We need each oth-er from day to day, We need each oth-er a-long the way;

He needs my love and my serv-ice, too, And I need Je-sus to guide me thro'.

Jesus of Calvary

Mrs. E. F. Thompson Copyright, 1928, by V. O. Stamps Virgil O. Stamps

1. I am employed by Je-sus, my King, True to His cause I'll
2. Souls are now lost in dark-ness and sin, Light of His love can't
3. When you have giv'n your life to the Lord, You will be glad and

be; (I will be;) Sin-ners I'll tell of the cross and the Lamb, Je-sus of
see; (they can't see;) Yet there is One who can save them to-day, Je-sus of
free; (glad and free;) He has prepared us a home o-ver there, Je-sus of

Cal-va-ry.

REFRAIN

Je - - - sus of Cal - va-ry Is the
Je-sus, my Lord, on Cal-va-ry
God.......... wants us all to be, Now re-
God wants us all hap-py to be,

hope of the soul,........ He died.......... that we
Anchored the hope of ev-'ry soul, Suf-fered and died,
deemed and made whole,....... Be (Omit.................)
Cleansed and redeemed and be made whole,

might be free And reach heav - - ens's fair goal;.........
we might be free, Win the great prize, heaven's fair goal, and now

Jesus of Calvary

blood - washed by Je - sus of Cal - va - ry.
Washed in the blood, Je-sus the Lamb who suffered on dark Cal-va-ry.

No. 129   When His Love Reached Me

James Rowe   S. H. Skelton, owner, 1929   S. H. Skelton

1. I was lone - ly and sad, I was far a-stray, And the path was too
2. All the sins that I bore are for-ev - er gone, And His child I shall
3. At His side I shall walk to the cit - y fair, That His face I at
4. Soul in sin and in doubt trust my Lord di-vine, Such a Friend He will

dark to see; But when Je - sus, my Lord, came to me that day,
al - ways be; I am press - ing a - long to that land of dawn,
last may see; In His glo - ry di - vine I shall ev - er share,
ev - er be; If you trust Him your soul as the stars shall shine,

D. S.—*All my fear passed a - way, for He filled my need,*

FINE REFRAIN

It was joy when His love reached me. It was joy,........ 'twas joy in-
It was joy, 'twas joy in-

It was joy when His love reached me.   D. S.

deed,........ .. When the Lord.... .... made me free;..........
deed, joy in - deed, When the Lord made me free, (pure and free;)

No. 130   Jesus is my Pilot

V. O. S.   Virgil O. Stamps, owner, 1920   **Virgil O. Stamps**

1. Je - sus is my Pi - lot, in the time of storm, He is shield- ing
2. When the Lord is near me, bil-lows wild may roll, And I'll fear no
3. When the Savior speaks, the winds and waves are still, An - gry seas of

1. time of storm,

me from ev - 'ry wild a - larm, When the wind is sweeping o'er the stormy
dan - ger, He will keep my soul, He has nev-er failed me, and He nev- er
life o - bey His bless-ed will, He will keep me safe tho' bil-lows wild may

Chorus

sea, I am safe for He is shield- ing me. He's
will, Close to Him I'm cling-ing, trust -ing still.
roar, Till I an -chor safe on heav -en's shore.
storm-y sea, On the stormy,

my Pi - lot, He is guid-ing me, my
troubled o-cean, I am free from all com-mo-tion,

soul from sin is ev - er free, He
and I am hap-py for I know that He will

Jesus is my Pilot

will guide me, guide me and no e- vil can be- tide me, for my

Pi - lot He will be, till I cross the dark and storm - y sea. the storm - y sea.

No. 131 Will You Meet Me in Glory-land?

Don Hooper Virgil O. Stamps, owner, 1923 **Virgil O. Stamps**

1. The Lord is near, I have no fear, I'm walk-ing with Him hand in hand;
2. I'm free from sin, I'm trusting in His prom-ise sweet, as best I can;
3. When life is o'er on that blest shore, And all the saved shall take their stand

:S: Fine

Then all is well, I'm glad to tell, Will you meet me (there) in glo- ry land?
O can you say, that some glad day I will meet you (there) in glo- ry land?
A -round the throne, in that sweet home, Will you then be (there) in glo- ry land?

D.S.—How glad I'd be, your face to see, Will you meet me (there) in glo- ry-land?

Chorus D. S.

Will you meet me (there) in glo -ry-land, Just o - ver on the gold-en strand?

No. 132   All is Well

James Rowe   V. O. Stamps, owner, 1924   **Virgil O. Stamps**

Bass prominent

1. Tho the way be thorn - y and the hills be steep,
1. Tho the way be thorn- y and the hills be steep,
2. Tho the might - y storms are sweeping on my soul,
3. Ev - er get - ting near - er to the pearl - y gate, All is

Yes, all is well,   is well with me; For I walk with
   For I'm liv - ing
well,   all is well,   With this sweet as-

Je - sus   who will safe-ly keep;
Je -sus who will safe - ly keep; All is well with me, all is
un - der His di - vine con - trol;
sur-ance I will watch and wait; All is well,

Chorus

well.   All is well, (I know,) all is well (be-low,) To the
   yes, all is well.   well (with me,) all is well, (I'm free,) For my

bless- ed One I'm clinging, of His love and mer-cy sing-ing, And my joy-bells
sins have been for- giv-en, By the One whose side was riv-en, So I'm go-ing

All Is Well

all are ring-ing, all is well; All is all is well.
home to heav-en, all is well; all is well.

No. 133

Harbor Bells

V. O. S.

Virgil O. Stamps, owner, 1925

Virgil O. Stamps

1. There is mu-sic in my soul to-day, For the Sav-ior pi-lots me;
2. Ev - er since the day I got on board, Cling-ing to the true life - line,
3. Some day, o - ver yon-der, safe at home, Where no bil-lows ev - er roll,

Har-bor bells are ring-ing o'er the way, And at home I soon shall be.
There has been a song for Christ my Lord, In this ransomed soul of mine.
I shall dwell in peace, no more to roam, With the Pi-lot of my soul.

Chorus

Bells are ring-ing, Cheer-ing me a-cross the foam;
glad-ness bring-ing,

All my sad-ness For my soul is near-ing home.
turns to glad-ness,

No. 134 Pray For Me

V. O. S.
V. O. Stamps, owner, 1923
Virgil O. Stamps

1. When you go a-lone at ev'-ning, At the close of
2. I am weak and ver-y wayward, Prone to err or
3. If my friends will go to Je-sus, In a pray'r for
4. Pray that we may meet each other, In the fair-er

1. When you go at the ev'ning,

ev-'ry day; Ask the Lord to guard and guide me,
prone to stray; And I need your in-ter-ces-sion
me each day; I am sure that He will help me
world above, Where we'll sing the praise of Je-sus,

Ask the Lord guard and guide me,

Chorus

As I tread......the pil-grim way. Pray for me, pray for
With the Lord......from day to day. Won't you pray for me?
Con-quer sin.........a-long the way.
For His nev - - - er - dy-ing love. Pray for me,

me, In-ter-cede for me in pray'r; When you go a-lone at
Won't yon pray for me? When you go

pray for me,

Pray For Me

rit.

ev'ning, Plead for me with Je-sus there.
at the ev'ning, Plead for me with Je-sus there.

No. 135

A Light on the River

James Rowe

V. O. Stamps, owner, 1928

Virgil O. Stamps

1. When I reach the bank of the si-lent stream, Not a shad-ow of
2. Tho' the waves roll high peace will fill my soul, For my Mas-ter and
3. I shall see the way to the oth-er shore, Where to wel-come me

fear there will be; For up-on the shore ev-er bright to gleam, There's a
Lord I shall see; And, that I may reach the e-ter-nal goal, There's a
dear ones will be; That my soul may pass ver-y safe-ly o'er, There's a

D.S.—have no fear when the night is near, There's a

Fine   Chorus

light on the riv-er for me.   There's a light on the riv-er for
a light there for me.   a

light on the riv-er for me.

D. S.

me,   And its brightness I ev-er shall see;   I shall
light there for me,   I ev-er shall see;

I'll Trust Him all the Way

"Though He slay me yet will I trust Him."—Job

James Rowe   Copyright, 1929, by V. O. Stamps   Virgil O. Stamps

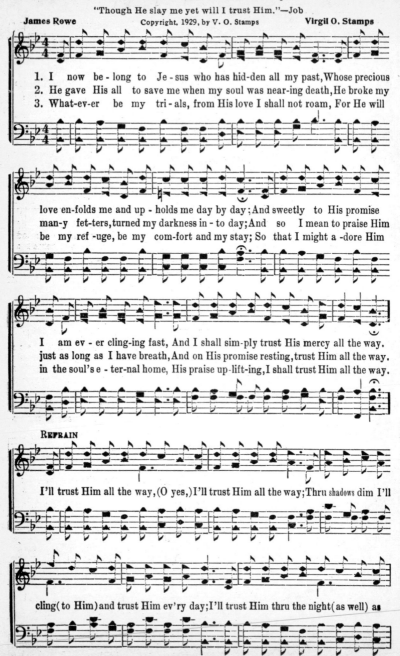

1. I now be-long to Je-sus who has hid-den all my past, Whose precious
2. He gave His all to save me when my soul was near-ing death, He broke my
3. What-ev-er be my tri-als, from His love I shall not roam, For He will

love en-folds me and up-holds me day by day; And sweetly to His promise
man-y fet-ters, turned my darkness in-to day; And so I mean to praise Him
be my ref-uge, be my com-fort and my stay; So that I might a-dore Him

I am ev-er cling-ing fast, And I shall sim-ply trust His mercy all the way.
just as long as I have breath, And on His promise resting, trust Him all the way.
in the soul's e-ter-nal home, His praise up-lift-ing, I shall trust Him all the way.

REFRAIN

I'll trust Him all the way, (O yes,) I'll trust Him all the way; Thru shadows dim I'll

cling (to Him) and trust Him ev'ry day; I'll trust Him thru the night (as well) as

I'll Trust Him all the Way

'neath the sun's bright ray; Yes, "Tho' He slay me I wil trust Him" all the way.

No. 137   CHRIST LEADS ME ON.

E. M. Bartlett.   Virgil O. Stamps.

1. Christ leads me on to higher ground, (to higher ground,) He shows the way to me,
2. Christ leads me on to broader fields, (to broader fields,) A lead-er true is He,
3. Christ leads me on tho'ways be rough (tho' ways be rough,) And dark the paths may be;

Since I in Him sal-va-tion found, (sal-va-tion found,) I know He lead-eth me.
Since I my soul to Him did yield, (to Him did yield,) I know He lead-eth me.
I trust in Him for grace enough, (for grace enough,) I know He lead-eth me.

CHORUS.

He leads me on, I trust in Him, His guid-ing hand I see,
gent-ly leads me on,

His spir-it walks with me each day, I know He lead-eth me.
Ho-ly Spir-it walks,

No. 138

The King I Love

James Rowe

V. O. Stamps, owner

Virgil O. Stamps

1. I sing of One from heav-en Who, to make me free, His precious blood has
2. I sing of One who cheers me, Lifts me when I fall, And who so quick-ly
3. I sing of One whose sto-ry Gladdens all my days; Of One whose love and

giv-en Up-on Mount Cal-va-ry. And I shall sing for-ev-er Of
hears me When His dear name I call. To Him my soul is cling-ing, As-
glo-ry The ho-ly an-gels praise. O bless-ed, pre-cious Je-sus, Dear

Him in realms a-bove With all who know my King be-low And trust His
sured that He is mine, And that I may from day to day A-bide in
Sav-ior of my soul! My joy 'twill be to sing of Thee While countless

Chorus

bound-less love. Yes, glo-ry to God! gone for-ev-er
love di-vine.
a-ges roll. My sins are gone for-ev-er

In the most won-der-ful flood Of Je-sus who did,
In the crim-son flood Of Him who

The King I Love

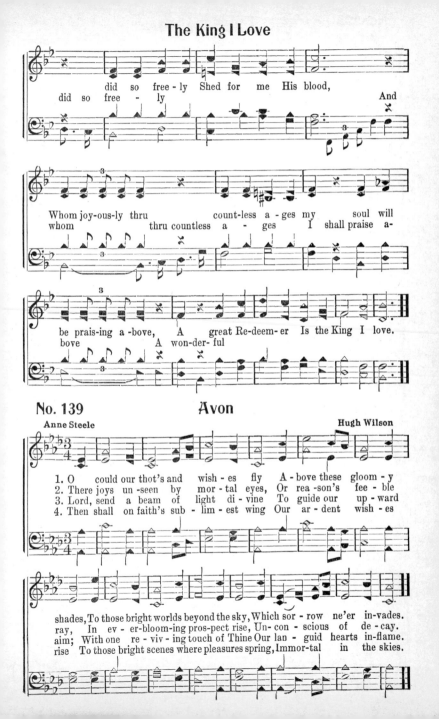

did so free-ly Shed for me His blood,
did so free-ly And

Whom joy-ous-ly thru count-less a-ges my soul will
whom thru countless a-ges I shall praise a-

be prais-ing a-bove, A great Re-deem-er Is the King I love.
bove A won-der-ful

No. 139   **Avon**

Anne Steele   Hugh Wilson

1. O could our thot's and wish-es fly A-bove these gloom-y
2. There joys un-seen by mor-tal eyes, Or rea-son's fee-ble
3. Lord, send a beam of light di-vine To guide our up-ward
4. Then shall on faith's sub-lim-est wing Our ar-dent wish-es

shades, To those bright worlds beyond the sky, Which sor-row ne'er in-vades.
ray, In ev-er-bloom-ing pros-pect rise, Un-con-scious of de-cay.
aim; With one re-viv-ing touch of Thine Our lan-guid hearts in-flame.
rise To those bright scenes where pleasures spring, Immor-tal in the skies.

Some Day in Glory

S. W. Jones   Virgil O. Stamps

Not too fast

1. Some day when life with me is o - ver And I shall face the judgment bar
2. Some day when Jesus bids me en - ter In - to the Shepherd's peaceful fold,
3. Some day I'll en-ter heaven's por-tals And meet my Sav-ior face to face,

Where God will judge the many faith-ful And those who drifted out a - far,
Tho I have been a way-worn pilgrim, I'll see the shining streets of gold
I'll live with friends and precious loved ones And those redeemed by sav-ing grace;

There I shall see most wondrous beauty And catch a glimpse of glory bright
Where Christ for me has built a mansion, Be-cause I trust-ed grace di-vine,
Then thru the gates of that fair cit - y In - to the joys that are in store,

D. S.—wondrous joy thruout the a - ges With Christ in glo - ry I shall share,
FINE

And hear the mighty ransomed cho-rus In that great land of pure delight.
I'll praise Him thru the endless a-ges, Where all His glo - ry shall be mine.
With Christ who still will own and love me, I'll dwell in peace for ev-er-more.

There I shall sing with saints and sages, Sweet songs of joy beyond compare.

CHORUS

Some day   I'll
Some day I'll en-ter that fair cit-y where Je - sus is the shin - ing light,

Some Day in Glory

go...........................
go on sweeping thru the por-tals in-to a place where comes no night,

D. S.

Where

No. 141

Is It Well With Your Soul?

James Rowe

V. O. Stamps, owner

Virgil O. Stamps

1. 'Mid the toil and strife of this bus - y life,   Is it well   with your soul?
2. Have you lost your sin? are you pure within?
3. Do you praise the love of the One a-bove? Is it well..... with your soul?....

Are you living right? should you die to-night?   Is it well with your soul?...
Are you at the side of the cru-ci -fied?
Will the crown be won and the Lord's "well done?" Is it well.... with your soul?...

Fine

D. S.—*Are you living right? should you die to-night? Is it well .. with your soul?*

CHORUS

It it well ... with your soul,.... Are you free,... glad and whole?....
    Is it well   with your soul?   Are you free,   glad and whole?

D. S.

No. 142 Like the Rainbow

J. R. Baxter, Jr.

Virgil O. Stamps

1. If you would make the world brighter As o'er life's pathway you tread,
2. If you would help bear the bur-dens Of the tired pilgrims be-low,
3. If you want friends here to miss you When you cross o-ver the tide,

If you would drive a - way sor - row, Hap-pi - ness 'round you spread;
If you would ban-ish their heart-aches, Make their path brightly glow;
If you want foot-prints be- hind you Safe- ly their feet to guide;

You must be faithful and earn - est, Look to the Sav-ior di - vine,
You must be read y to help them See thru each e - vil de - sign,
You must be careful, my broth - er, Lest you should waste precious time,

You must be true in all you do, Just like the rain-bow shine.
Show them the way, teach them to pray, Just like the rain-bow shine.
Do- ing your best, un- der each test, Just like the rain-bow shine.

CHORUS

Troubles, ... bur-dens, . . . cheer those who pine;
Troubles to share, bur- dens to bear, Help cheer the souls who pine: . . . .

Like the Rainbow

Tell-ing,...... look-ing,..... let your light shine.
Tell-ing of love, look-ing a - bove, Just like the rain-bow shine..........

No. 143   He Will Save You

Copyright, 1931, by The Stamps-Baxter Music Co.,
in "Tuneful Praise" V. O. Stamps, owner

Sid Talley   Virgil O. Stamps

1. Look to Je-sus, He will save you, Trust the mer-its of His grace;
2. Do not lin-ger an - y lon-ger, Ask of Him just what you will,
3. Come to Him with all your sorrows, He can heal each broken heart;

He is a - ble to re-lieve you When you meet Him face to face.
For He knoweth ev-'ry sorrow, He your life with joy can fill.....
Let Him en-ter while He's pleading, Do not tell Him to de-part.....

CHORUS

He is a - ble to re-lieve you From each sorrow of the past,....

the past,

Let His ho - ly spir- it guide you Till you reach the home at last.

No. 144

He Said If I Be Lifted Up

Arr. copyright. 1938, by The Stamps-Baxter Music Co.

C. E. P. Arr. by J. R. B., Jr.   Chas. H. Pace, Arr. by V. O. Stamps

1. Down in the val-ley while on my knees I asked my Je-sus hear me
2. My Je-sus told me, when things go wrong, Just keep on pray-ing all day
3. When I am lone-ly, when I am sad, My Je-sus comes and makes me

please, He promised that He'd take care of me, If I would lift Him up.
long, I'll fight your battles, I'll make you strong, If you will lift me up.
glad; He is the dear-est friend I have had, I want to lift Him up.

Chorus

He said if I be lift-ed up, He said if
He said if I be lift-ed up,

I be lift-ed up; I'll be your fa-ther, I'll
He said if I be lift-ed up;

be your mother, I'll be your sis-ter and your brother,
brother, He said if

He Said If I Be Lifted Up

He said if I be lift-ed up,
be lifted up,
I'll bring joy
joy, joy
to your soul.

No. 145 I Know My Name Is There

Luke 10: 20.

D. S. WARNER

CONTROLLED BY R. E. WINSET

R. E. WARREN

1. My name is in the Book of Life, O bless the name of Je - sus!
2. My name once stood with sinners, lost, And bore a pain - ful rec - ord;
3. Yet in-ward troub-le oft - en cast A shad-ow o'er my ti - tle;
4. While oth-ers climb thro' worldly strife, To carve a name of hon - or,

I rise a-bove all doubt and strife, And read my ti - tle clear.
But by His blood the Sav - ior cross'd, And placed it on His roll.
But now with full sal - va - tion blest, Praise God! it's ev - er clear.
High up in heav-en's Book of Life, My name is writ - ten there.

Chorus

I know,........ I know...... my name........ is there; is there;
I know, I tru - ly know,   I know my name is there;

I know,...... I know........ my name is writ - ten there.
I know my name is there,

No. 146 Sing Along Your Way

George O. Webster

Virgil O. Stamps

1. There's a song of cheer   For the dark-est day,   Tho the
2. Sing your song of cheer   'Long the toilsome road,   Tho the
3. Sing a song of cheer   Oth-ers need your song;   Bur-dened

clouds be near   They will break a - way;   It will not be
day be drear,   Light-er grows the load;   Just a lilt of
souls are near,   You can make them strong;   Bright-er grows the

long   Ere you see the blue;   Sing a cheer - y song
song   Will your strength renew,   All your way a - long
way,   Near-er grows the blue   Ech-oes of your lay

REFRAIN

Till the sun shines thro'.Song   will Brighten a dr ear - y road,
Song will heart-en you.
Com - ing back to you. O a hap-py song,

Song   will light - en a heav - y load;Song   will
Yes, a hap-py song,   And a hap - py song

Sing Along Your Way

short-en the long-est day, Sing a - long your way,

Sing a - long your way, sing along your way.

Sing a - long the way.

No. 147

Twill All Be Glory

M. H. M.

M. H. McKEE, OWNER. 1927

M. H. McKee

Deliberately

1. While toil-ing on-ward a-long life's road Be-neath a bur-den of care,
2. It keeps me hap-py, the whole day long To know the cit - y is near,
3. Oh, what a meet-ing 'twill be some day With-in the cit - y so fair

A glad hope light-ens the heav-y load: 'Twill all be glo - ry up there.
So close-ly bor-ders the land of song, 'Twill all be glo - ry up there.
When pain and sor-row shall flee away, 'Twill all be glo - ry up there.

REFRAIN.

'Twill all be glo - ry up there, ... Where all is won-drous-ly fair; ....
up there, bright and fair;

rit.

In heav-en a-bove, Blest cit-y of love, 'Twill all be glo-ry up there. (up there.)

Lord, Let Me Serve

Laurene Highfield   Virgil O. Stamps, owner   **Virgil O. Stamps**

Baritone Solo and Quartet

1. I do not ask for hap-py days, For eas-y tasks and joy-crowned ways, I on-ly ask that I may be Of use, my Lord and Christ, to Thee.
2. I do not long for high re-nown, I on-ly crave a liv-ing crown, Set with the gems that I have earned, The souls of men from e-vil turned.
3. I do not ask for wealth or fame, But that I may not put to shame, Nor cru-ci-fy my Lord a-new, By be-ing faith-less or un-true.

CHORUS

Lord, let me serve.......... and faith-ful be, Lord, let me hum-bly fol-low Thee; Make in Thy ranks.......... a place for me,

Lord, let me serve and faith-ful be, Lord, let me hum-bly fol-low Thee; Make in Thy ranks.......... (a place for me..........)

Lord, Let Me Serve

And keep me true and loy - al, true and loy - al.

And keep me true and loy - al....

No. 149

Love Divine Is Mine

James Rowe
C. D. Williams, owner
C. D. Williams

1. Hap - py songs I sing to - day, As I press a - long my way,
2. What are grief and care to me, If the Fount of love is free?
3. Hap - py songs are mine to - day, Hap - py songs will with me stay;

For this ran-somed soul of mine O - ver-flows with love di - vine.
What are sor - row and dis - tress, If my Sav - ior waits to bless?
Joy will ev - er - more be mine, If I cling to love di - vine.

Chorus

Love di - vine, re - deem - ing love! Pre-cious gift of God a - bove!

This my sweet - est song will be Thru the glad e - ter - ni - ty.

Awake and Sing

James Wells Copyright, 1931, by V. O. Stamps Virgil O. Stamps

1. The light is breaking in the east (the east) And soon will come the dawn, The rose un-folds its petals sweet, (so sweet,) The dew is on the lawn..... A-wake, a-wake, A-

2. The birds a-wak-en with the dawn (the dawn) And watch the east a-flame, And sweet they sing till woodlands ring (yes, ring) Glad praise un-to His name..... A - wake, a - wake,

3. The sun a gold-en globe ap-pears (appears) And sends a shin-ing ray, With joy it comes to tell the world, (the world,) A-wake! a-wake! 'tis day...... A - wake, a - wake,

CHORUS

wake and car-ols sing, A-wake, awake, a-wake and sing A car-ol to the King; A-wake, a-wake, The east is all a-flame, the King; A-wake, a-wake,

Awake and Sing

A-wake! a-wake! a-wake and sing Ho - san - nas to His name,.....
Ho - ly name.

No. 151 SEND ME

James Rowe

Virgil O. Stamps

1. Is there a task waiting somewhere to-day? Help-ful I want to be;
2. Is there a bur-den that I may make light—Someone from grief to free?
3. Is there a heart needing comfort and cheer—Tossed on life's troubled sea?

Is there a broth-er to help on the way? Mas-ter and Friend, send me.
Is there a friend who is lost in the night? Mas-ter and Friend, send me.
That in Thy like-ness my soul may ap-pear, Mas-ter and Friend, send me.

CHORUS.

Mas-ter, send me, Mas-ter, send me, Help-ful in-deed I want to be;

Use me, I pray, for Thy glo-ry to-day; Mas-ter and Lord, send me.......
send me.

Virgil O. Stamps, Timpson Tex., 1921. Used by per.

No. 152   He Bore It All

J. R. Baxter, Jr.   COPYRIGHT, 1926, BY V. O. STAMPS   Virgil O. Stamps

1. My pre-cious Sav-ior suf-fered pain and ag - o - ny, He bore it
2. They placed a crown of thorns up - on my Sav-ior's head,
3. Up Cal-v'ry's hill in shame the bless - ed Sav-ior trod,

all .... that I might live; .... He broke the bonds of
By cru - el man with
free - ly bore it all   I with Him might live; Between two thieves they

sin and set the cap - tive free,   all that I might
spear His side was pierced and bled,   cru - ci - fied the Son of God, He bore it all that I might

FINE   REFRAIN

in His presence live. He bore it all   that   I might see His
live ....   Je - sus bore it all,

shin - ing face,   Free - ly bore it all
see His shin-ing face, He bore it all .... that I might

He Bore It All

D. S.

I with Him might live; I stood condemned to die but Je-sus took my place,
live; .... stood condemned to die free-ly took my place

No. 153   It Does Not Pay

James Rowe   Copyright, 1926, by V. O. Stamps   Virgil O. Stamps

rit.

1. Why spend your life with God at strife, In pleasure's downward way? ....
2. You live in dread of years a - head, And years all thrown a - way; ....
3. With - in your breast remains un- rest, For night is on its way; ....
4. O soul, be wise, a - wake, a- rise! Be pardoned while you may; ....

You on - ly find dis-tress of mind, And know it does not pay.......
True joys are missed, you just ex- ist, And know it does not pay.......
And yet you roam a-way from home, You know it does not pay.......
Let Je - sus in and turn from sin, You know it does not pay.......

Chorus

You know it does not pay, You lose from day to day;
it does not pay, ... from day to day; ......

rit.   *m*   *f*   *a tempo*   *rit.*

Your steps re-trace, be saved by grace, You know it does not pay.......
does not pay.

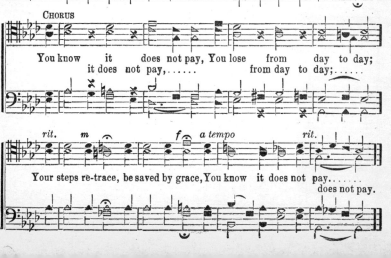

No. 154   He is Leading Me

Luther G. Presley   Virgil O. Stamps

1. Go-ing a-long, (with Je-sus) sing-ing a song, (so hap-py,) The weight of
2. To glo-ry land, (He's leading,) to mansions grand, (we're speeding) Where I shall
3. The way is bright, (with heaven's) won-der-ful light, (since He has) Lift-ed the

sadness from my heart has flown; (for-ev-er;) I now re-joice (and praise Him)
join the hap-py ransomed throng; (in heav-en:) On that bright shore (e-ter-nal)
clouds that hid the az-ure hue; (and He is) Leading me straight, (to heaven's)

with heart and voice, (for He is) Tru-ly the sweet-est Friend I've ev-er known.
for-ev-er-more, (in glo-ry,) With an-gels I shall sing the glad new song.
beau-ti-ful gate, (where that bright) Cit-y of gold with Him I soon shall view.

CHORUS

All glo - - - ry to His name, ... The days that were dreary
All glo-ry and hon-or to His bless-ed name,

now are cheer-y since He came; At home............... I soon shall
                     At home with the saved I soon shall

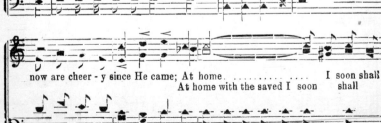

He is Leading Me

be,..... For He a - lone leads me.....
be, shall be, For this blessed Friend till life here shall end is lead-ing me.

No. 155 Over and Over Again

Rev. Alfred Barratt

Virgil O. Stamps, owner, 1924

Virgil O. Stamps

1. Once my heart was o'er-burdened with care, Now my troubles are eas-y to
2. I was bound, but He brought me re-lease, He has made all my sor-rows to
3. There is noth-ing to cause me to fear When the gloom and the darkness ap-
4. I will tell of His won-der-ful grace, Till I en-ter that beau-ti-ful

bear; For the Sav-ior has answered my pray'r O - ver and o - ver a-
cease; He is fill-ing my soul with His peace, O - ver and o - ver a-
pear; For His presence is con-stant-ly near, O - ver and o - ver a-
place; Where with joy I shall look on His face, O - ver and o - ver a-

D. S.—o - ver and o - ver a-

FINE. CHORUS

gain...... O - ver and o - ver and o - ver a - gain, (yes,) O - ver and

gain......

D. S.

o - ver a - gain; When I'm lone-ly and sad, Then His love makes me glad, Just

No. 156 Some of These Days

Copyright, 1934, by The Stamps-Baxter Music Co.,
in "Leading Light"

W. E. Edmiaston Virgil O. Stamps

1. I'm wait-ing for the sum-mons that shall call me to life's goal,
2. I'll leave my load of cares and sor-rows all down here be-low,
3. I know my friends down here will weep when I am called a-bove,

Some of these days,.......... it won't be long;....... And
    I know it won't be long; And
Some of these days, it won't be long; But

when it comes I'll an-swer it with gladness in my soul, Some of these
go to join that cho-rus where God's lovelight is a-glow,
I'll be wait-ing for their com-ing in that home of love,

D. S.—*Some of these*

FINE CHORUS

days,.............. it won't be long........ Some of these
O some of these days, I know it won't be long.
Some of these days, it won't be long.

days, ... it won't be long......

days,........ it won't be long,..... Some of these days,..... I'll sing the
Some of these days it won't be long, Some of these days,

Some of These Days

hal-le -lu -jah song With saints a - bove........ ..... where all is love,.....
With saints a-bove where all is love,

No. 157 Keep Your Own Corner Bright

James Rowe   V. O. Stamps, owner   Virgil O. Stamps

1. Do not grieve day by day just because o er the way E - vil shadows some
2. Would you do your own part, with your hands and your heart, On the way to the
3. You may long to give light un - to all lost in night, Or to shield all the

heart may de - file; But to show you are true and your whole du - ty do.
beau - ti - ful Isle; Give to those who are near light and cour-age and cheer,
foe would de - file; But your share you will do for the Mas - ter if you

D. S.—Nev - er mind pla - ces far, serve the Lord where you are,

FINE   CHORUS

Keep your own cor-ner bright all the while, Keep your own cor - ner bright,
Keep your corner bright,

Keep your own cor-ner bright all the while.

all the while,   Giv - ing to oth - ers the light of your smile;
all the while,   Give the lost the

No. 158   Sparkling Gems

V. O. S.

Virgil O. Stamps

1. Sparkling gems of *Truth* in the book di-vine, Safe will guide your feet as they're
2. Sparkling gems of *Light* from the word of God, Lighted up the path that the
3. Sparkling gems of *Hope* in the Christian's breast, Drive away all fear, bringing

guid-ing mine; In the up-ward way, to the land of day, Spark-ling
pil-grim trod; Just the same to-day, they will light the way, Spark-ling
per-fect rest; In a lit-tle while, we shall see His smile, Spark-ling

REFRAIN

gems of *Truth* shine on. Sparkling gems of *Truth*, Sparkling gems of *Light*,
gems of *Light* shine on.
gems of *Hope* shine on. Gems of *Truth* and

Sparkling gems of *Hope*, Guide us thru the night,
Light and *Hope*, Coming from a-bove,

fill the earth with love, Gems of *Truth* and *Light* and *Hope* shine on.

I'll Be List'ning

Arr.   Arr. by V. O. STAMPS

1. When the Sav-ior calls I will an - swer, When He calls for me I will
2. If my heart is right when He calls me, If my heart is right I will
3. If my robe is white when He calls me, If my robe is white I will

hear; When the Sav - ior calls I will an - swer, I'll be somewhere
hear; If my heart is right when He calls me, I'll be somewhere
hear; If my robe is white when He calls me, I'll be somewhere

CHORUS

list'ning for my name.
list'ning for my name. I'll be somewhere list'ning, I'll be somewhere list'ning,
list'ning for my name.

I'll be somewhere list'ning for my name;   I'll be somewhere
                            yes, for my name;

list'ning, I'll be somewhere list'ning, I'll be somewhere list'ning for my name.

Endless Joy is Waiting

James Rowe Copyright, 1927, by V. O. Stamps Virgil O. Stamps

1. Not a sign of sor-row there will be to-mor-row,
2. No one will be wea-ry, not one path be drear-y,
3. With the saints and sa-ges we shall spend the a-ges,

Where the Master's glo-ry we shall share;........... (For) By the crys-tal
Life will be for-ev-er sweet and fair;........... (Yes,) For with dear ones
And the bless-ed crown of glo-ry wear;........... (Then) Tempted, burdened

1. Where the Mas-ter's glo-ry we shall share;

D. S.— We shall sing the

riv-er we shall rest for-ev-er, End-less joy is
sing-ing and our joy-bells ring-ing,
nev-er, we shall be for-ev-er, End-less joy is wait-ing o-ver

sto-ry and shall share His glo-ry, End-less joy is wait-ing o-ver

FINE REFRAIN

wait-ing o-ver there. End-less joy is wait-ing o-ver there,
there............... End-less joy is wait-ing o-ver there,...........

there.............

D. S.

There is peace and rest be-yond com-pare;
And there's comfort peace and rest beyond compare;........... For

'TWILL NOT BE LONG

V. O. S.

Virgil O. Stamps

DUET Slow

1. Some day the cares of life will rise, Some day we'll be in
2. The toils of life will soon be past, Our bur-dens at His
3. Our loved ones in that home we'll see, At rest with them we'll

Par - a - dise; Then our dear Lord will right each wrong,
feet we'll cast; Then right shall take the place of wrong,
ev - er be; In dreams some-times I hear their song,

CHORUS *All Parts*
Faster

Oh! praise His name, 'twill not be long. 'Twill not be long, 'twill not be
Oh! hap-py tho't, 'twill not be long.
We soon shall meet, 'twill not be long. 'Twill not be long, 'twill

long 'Till right shall take the place of wrong; Look up and
not be long, 'Till right shall take the place of wrong; Look

smile, and sing a song, Oh, praise the Lord, 'twill not be long......
up and smile, and sing a song, Oh, praise the Lord, 'twill not be long.

No. 162   When I Cross the River

SPIRITUAL

J. W. Sykes   Virgil O. Stamps

1. I am work-ing for my Sav-ior ev'-ry pass-ing hour, I am
2. O if you are not con-vert-ed, do not know His love, You had
3. I am on my way to glo-ry, I am heav'n-ward bound, And I'll

trust-ing in the Ho-ly Spir-it's pow'r;.. So when this life is o-ver,
bet-ter ask for-give-ness from a-bove;... If you have no re-lig-ion,
nev-er let old Sa-tan turn me round;.. 'Cause in that res-ur-rec-tion,

FINE

I'll go home to stay, I want to cross the riv-er some sweet day....
nor been born a-gain, You can-not cross the riv-er my dear friend....
when the trump shall call, I want to see my Sav-ior first of all.......

D. S.—When I cross the riv-er o-ver there.....

CHORUS

When I cross the riv-er, that wide riv-er of Jor-dan, I will meet my friends and

D. S.

loved ones there; I'll shake hands with my mother, my father, sister and brother,

I'M LIVING ON THE ROCK

James Rowe   Virgil O. Stamps

1. Mighty storms a-round me sweeping, Fail to cause me an-y fear, For I'm
2. Ma-ny wrecks I see a-round me, But no harm can come to me, For I'm
3. Sin-ner, lest the waves o'erwhelm you, Make my ref-uge now your own, For I'm

I am liv-ing, yes, I'm liv-ing on the Rock; Day and night I feel the
I am free from con-dem-
liv - - - ing on the Rock;........... Here the sun is al-ways

D.S.—Storms are un-der His con-

presence Of my soul's Re-deem-er near, I am liv-ing,
na-tion, And for-ev-er safe shall be,
shin-ing, Here the joys of life are known, For I'm liv - - - - ing

trol, and They can nev-er reach my soul, For I'm liv - - - - ing

yes, I'm liv-ing on the Rock. I am liv-ing, yes, I'm
on the Rock .... I am liv - - - - ing on the

Fine. CHORUS.

I am liv-ing

D. S.

liv-ing on the Rock, That withstandeth, that withstandeth ev'ry shock,
Rock, ... That withstand - - - eth ev-'ry shock,.........

on the Rock, That with-stand-eth ev-'ry shock;

No. 164   WIN THEM FOR JESUS

Geo. W. Winningham.

Virgil O. Stamps

1. Out in the highways in sin and despair Mil-lions to e-vil still cling,
2. Mil-lions are bow-ing to i-dols each year, Millions who hear not the word;
3. Mil-lions are lost to the Mas-ter to-day, Mil-lions who know not His love;

Knowing not Je-sus, His love and His care; Oh win them for Je-sus the King.
Bring to their temples our Saviour so dear; Oh win them for Je-sus the Lord.
Tell them the sto-ry; yes, has-ten a-way; Oh win them for Je-sus a-bove.

CHORUS

Win........ them for Him,........ Oh, win.......... them for
Win them for Him, go and win them to-day, Oh, win them to-day, go and

Him,.......... Oh, help them to smile and to sing;........ Point them
win them to-day, ev-er sing;

rit.

a-bove to the Sav-iour of love, Oh, win them for Je-sus the King.

Virgil O. Stamps, owner, Timpson, Tex., 1921

No. 165   YOUR REDEEMER CARES

James Rowe

Virgil O. Stamps

1. There are times when you sigh and when tears fill the eye, And you fear you may
2. There are times when you dread all the tri-als a-head, On-ly troub-le and
3. Ev-'ry day, all the way, be your cares what they may, Your Re-deem-er will

fail to be true; But, O soul, wor-ry not, com-fort take from the tho't:
care seem in view; But be brave and press on 'tward the king-dom of dawn;
pi-lot you thro'; Rest your faith on His love, rest is wait-ing a-bove:

CHORUS

Your Re-deem-er is car-ing for you. He is car-ing for you, tri-als

bear-ing for you, To your soul He will al-ways be true; He is near ev-

'ry day, trust His love all the way; Your Re-deemer is car-ing for you.

I'M GOING HOME

VIRGIL O. STAMPS

DUET *Slow*

1. In fan - cy now I see my home, Where Jesus dwells, where angels roam,
2. I see the streets of pur - est gold, The Jas-per walls of wealth un-told;
3. Oh, hap-py day when I shall be From sin and sor - row ev - er free;

rit.

And all my friends who've gone before, Are safe up there for ev - er - more.
I see the Lord, now as He stands, Call-ing to me with out-stretched hands.
And dwell a-mong my friends of yore, And sing to Christ for ev - er - more.

CHORUS *Faster*

I'm go - ing home, ... I'm go - ing home, ... With an - gels
I'm go-ing home,   I'm go-ing home,

there .... I'll sing; .... We'll sing to Him .... who reigns su -
With angels there   so sweetly sing;   We'll sing to Him

preme, ... And make the heav - ens ring. ....
Who reigns supreme, And make the heavens loud-ly ring, yes, loud with music ring.
     make the heavens ring,

there we'll make the heavens ring.

No. 167   I'M SAILING ON

V. O. S.

Virgil O. Stamps

1. I am safe-ly sail-ing a-cross the tide, And my barque is breasting
2. I've a chart and com-pass that can-not fail, I am shouting hap-py
3. Soon the har-bor lights on the shore I'll see, With my loved ones ev-er

the wa-ters wide; Soon the face of Je-sus my Lord I'll see, I'm
as on I sail; Knowing Je-sus ev-er with me will be, I'm
at home I'll be; From the snares of sin I will then be free, I'm

CHORUS

sail-ing on to e-ter-ni-ty. I'm sailing (yes I'm) sailing up-on life's sea,

I'm sail-ing on to e-ter-ni-ty bil-lows pow'rless to
I'm glad-ly sail-ing on to the raging now are

harm my soul, For my ship is (ev-er) un-der the Lord's con-trol.

RALLY FOR JESUS

V. O. S.

VIRGIL O. STAMPS.

1. Ral - ly for Je - sus the Sav - ior and King, Sol-diers are need-ed to
2. Loud calls the bu - gle, Oh, haste to the fray, Come join your comrades and
3. Ral - ly, oh sol-diers, the call is to you, Foes are as - sail-ing the

bat - tle for right   Forward to con-quer, o'er-com-ing each foe,
use all your might;   Foes are ad-vanc-ing, we must win the day,
for - ces of right;   Keep - ing the cause of the Sav-iour in view,

Oh, has-ten,

CHORUS

Ral - ly, sol-diers, and fight! fight! fight! Sol-diers, ral - ly to-day, go

forth to the fray, Go, know-ing your cause is right;   For-ward to

Oh, has-ten,

con-quer o'er com-ing each foe, Ral - ly, sol-diers, and fight! fight! fight!

Somebody Stumbling Over You

J. M. Cain   Virgil O. Stamps

1. Do you want wand'ring souls saved, my brother? Shun the wrong and the right always
2. Is your name on the church book, my brother? Are you watching the things that you
3. Do you claim you're a Christian, my broth-er? Are you doing the things Christ would

Slower

do; But if you should go a-stray, oth-ers then would lose the way, There'd be
do? If you live a sin-ful life, filled with en - vy, shame and strife, There is
do? If you are not liv-ing right, you're im-per-fect in His sight, There is
Hum............... hum...............

FINE   **REFRAIN**

some-bod-y stumbling ov-er you.   Some - - bod-y
There is some-bod-y stumbling ov - er

D. S.-some-bod-y stumbling ov - er you.

stumbling ov-er you,   Now   watch-ing   the course that you pursue;
you,   They are watching the course that you pur-sue;.............

Slower   *D. S.*

If your life is filled with sin that su-preme-ly rules with-in, There is
Hum...............   hum...............

No. 170 You Must Come in at the Door

As sung on Victor Record, No. 21722, by Stamps and Yandell

Copyright, 1929, by V. O. Stamps and M. L. Yandell

Arr. by Stamps and Yandell

Chorus

My Lord it's so high, you can't get o - ver it, So low, you can't get under it,

So wide, you can't go a - round it, You must come in at the door.

Bass Solo

1. Good morn - ing, fel - low pil - grims,........ You ask me
2. You may talk a - bout me, my broth - er, ... Just as much as
3. You ask me what's the mat - ter with the church, That we can't
4. O the Bap - tists go by wa - ter,........ The Meth - o - dists

where I'm bound, I'm trav' - ling to a
ev - er you please, But if I men - tion your
hear a shout, There are sin - ners in the a - men
go by land, But I tell you, friends, if you

D. C.

beau - ti - ful land, There to wear a robe and crown.
name at all, It'll be when I'm on my knees.
cor - ner, my friend, That ought to be turned out.
want to get to heav'n, You got - a go hand in hand.

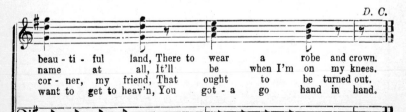

No. 171 I've Been Invited to a Jubilee

SPIRITUAL

Arr. V O. S.   Copyright, 1927, by V. O. Stamps   Virgil O. Stamps

Bass. *Ad lib.*

1. Broth-er, when I get to heav'n I shall sing and shout, Ju-bi-lee,
2. Broth-er, Sa-tan is a liar and a con-jur-er, too,
3. Sa-tan is just like a snake crawling in the grass,
4. What's the mat-ter in the church that we don't hear a shout?

ju-bi-lee; For there won't be an-y-bod-y there to
glo-ry, If you don't watch very close he will
Al-ways hid-ing close by where the
sweet story; Sin-ners in the a-men cor-ner ought to

put me out, Won't that be a hap-py ju-bi-lee?
con-jure you, You will miss the hap-py ju-bi-lee.
Chris-tians pass, Tries to make them miss the ju-bi-lee.
be turned out, Then we'd have a hap-py ju-bi-lee.

CHORUS*

Ju-bi-lee,............. ju-bi-lee,.......... I've been in-vit-ed
Ju-bi-lee,............. ju-bi-lee,

to a ju-bi-lee in heav-en aft-er-while;
(Omit............) heav-en aft-er-while.

*The rest preceding the chorus may be omitted if desired.

No. 172 I Ain't A Gonna Let Satan Turn Me 'Roun'

SPIRITUAL

Copyright, 1932, by V. O. Stamps

V. O. S.

Virgil O. Stamps

1. I've left the land of E-gypt, I'm bound for Canaan's sho', I'm go-in' to a
2. Just take a tip from Lot's wife who started well, you know, The Lord had told them
3. The Lord told brother Jo-nah, a long, long time a-go, To go and preach and

lan' where milk an' hon-ey flow; When I cross o-ver Jor-dan, I
all to leave that place of woe; She turned and looked a-roun', a
pray in Nin-e-veh, you know; But he at once set sail, and

know I'll wear a crown, 'Cause I ain't a gon-na let Sa-tan turn me 'roun'.
pil-lar of salt was foun', 'Cause she went and let ol' Sa-tan turn her 'roun'.
landed in the belly of the whale, 'Cause he went and let ol' Sa-tan turn him 'roun'.

CHORUS

No, I ain't a gon-na let Sa-tan turn me 'roun', ... No, I
turn me 'roun',

ain't a gon-na let Sa-tan turn me 'roun'; I've start-ed to heav-en,

I Ain't A Gonna Let Satan Turn Me 'Roun'

I am glo-ry boun', And I ain't a gon-na let Sa-tan turn me 'roun'.

No. 173   Steal Away

Arr.   Arr. by V. O. STAMPS

Steal a-way,........ Steal a-way,........ Steal a-way to
Steal a-way, Steal a-way,

Je-sus; Steal a-way,........ Steal a-way home, I ain' got long to
Steal a-way,

FINE

stay here.
1. My Lord calls me, He calls me by the thun-der,
2. Green trees bend-ing, Poor sin-ners stand a trem-blin',
3. My Lord calls me, He call me by the light-nin',

D.C.

The trum-pet sounds with-in a my soul, I ain' got long to stay here.

No. 174 You Gotta Live Your Religion Every Day

(SPIRITUAL)

S. B. Clark
1st and Chorus by V. O. S.
Copyright, 1933, by V. O. Stamps
Virgil O. Stamps

1. Some peo-ple go to church on Sun-day and stand up there and shout, And
2. O when you go to church on Sun-day and they pass the plate aroun', Jes'
3. Some folks in summertime get hap-py when re-vi-val time is on, O
4. Now take the case of Brother Dan-iel who lived long, long a-go, They

then they go to work on Mon-day and leave the Sav-ior out; They
dig rite down in-to your pock-et, don't shake your head and frown; Don't
how they shout and praise the Sav-ior and sing of heav'n and home; But
cast him in a den of li-ons, the sto-ry you all know; But

think that they have done their duty and to the Lord they have been true, But
turn that measly two-bits o-ver and hunt that little penny be-low, For you'll
when the summer-time is o-ver the weather gets cold in fall, You'll
Daniel lived the true re-li-gion and t'ward Je-ru-sa-lem did pray, So the

find when they reach the judgment, their one day re-li-gion won't do.
find that your penny re-li-gion, won't take you to the gold-en sho'!
find that the summer-time Christian don't live his re-li-gion at all.
Lord, Brother Daniel de-liv-ered from the den of hungry li-ons that day.

CHORUS

You got-ta live your re-li-gion ev'ry day, (ev'ry day,) You gotta live your re-

You Gotta Live Your Religion Every Day

-li-gion ev'ry day; (ev'ry day;) On Monday, Tuesday, Wednesday, Thursday, **Friday,**

Sat-ur-day, **Sunday,** You gotta live your re - li-gion ev-'ry day. (ev'ry day.)

No. 175   They Scandalized my Name
(Mixed Quartet)

Arr. V. O. S.   Arr. copyright, 1930, by V. O. Stamps   **Arr. by Virgil O. Stamps**

I met a (sis-ter / brother / preacher / dea-con) the other day, I gave (her / him) my right hand And just as
Hum...............

soon   as   ev-er my back was turned (she / he) scandalized my name.
Just as soon as   *Hum......................*

CHORUS   1   2   **FINE**

Call that religion? No! No! Call that religion? No! No!
         (Omit.... ....) Scandalized **my name.**
                                                my name.

No. 176 Massa's in de Cold, Cold Ground

Arr. copyright, 1929, by V. O. Stamps and J. R. Baxter, Jr.
Arr. by Stamps and Baxter

Massa's in de Cold, Cold Ground

pink-a ping ping pink-a ping ping pink-a ping ping pink-a ping ping pink-a ping ping
mound,   Dere   ole massa am a sleep-
shore,   Now   de summer days am com-
flow;   Try   to drive a - way my sor-

pong   pong pong pong Pong   pong   pong

pink-a ping ping Pink-a ping ping ping ping pink-a ping ping ping
ing,   Sleeping   in de cold, cold   ground.
ing,   Mas-sa   neb-ber calls no   more.
row   Picking   on de ole ban - jo.

pong   Pong   pong pong pong   pong pong pong

Chorus

Pink-a ping ping ping ping pink-a ping ping pink-a ping ping Ping ping ping
Down   in de corn - field   Hear dat mourn-

Pong   pong pong pong   pong   Pong pong pong

ping   pink-a ping ping pink-a ping ping Pink-a ping ping pink-a ping ping
ful sound,   All   de darkies am a

pong pong pong pong ponk-a pong pong pong pong Pong   pong.

de darkies weep,
weep - - ing, Massas's in de cold, cold ground.   ground.

*Use second ending for last time only

INDEX